THREE ICELANDIC SAGAS

THREE
ICELANDIC SAGAS

Gunnlaugs saga ormstungu

TRANSLATED BY M. H. SCARGILL

Bandamanna saga
Droplaugarsona saga

TRANSLATED BY MARGARET SCHLAUCH

ILLUSTRATIONS BY H. G. GLYDE, A.R.C.A.

1950

PRINCETON UNIVERSITY PRESS, PRINCETON, NEW JERSEY

FOR THE AMERICAN-SCANDINAVIAN FOUNDATION

NEW YORK

PRINTED IN THE UNITED STATES OF AMERICA
BY PRINCETON UNIVERSITY PRESS AT PRINCETON, NEW JERSEY
FRONTISPIECE PRINTED IN THE NETHERLANDS
BY VAN LEER AT AMSTERDAM

CONTENTS

A Poet's Love
The Saga of Gunnlaug and Hrafn

GUNNLAUGS SAGA ORMSTUNGU

The saga is translated from the Old Icelandic of a man who remains unknown. Some people have claimed that he was Ari the Wise[1] or, at any rate, a settler in Borgarfjord.

TRANSLATED BY M. H. SCARGILL

INTRODUCTION

THE *Saga of Gunnlaug and Hrafn* belongs to a group of stories about the Icelandic settlers in Borgarfjord, and it was probably told and perhaps later written down by some man from that district in Iceland. It tells of the tragic love of Gunnlaug for Helga—"the loveliest woman there has ever been in Iceland." The story has always attracted great attention. Perhaps it is the tragic dignity of the fair Helga that holds one reader, perhaps it is the impetuous figure of Gunnlaug that holds another. Certainly the skill of the narrator makes a tale to draw men from the chimney corner. Sir Philip Sydney himself would no doubt have approved of Gunnlaug and his rival Hrafn, for they are very much like Renaissance poets and warriors.

Several sagas have a poet for their hero, but such an insistence on love as is found in this story is not common, particularly in the longer sagas. The unity of the *Saga of Gunnlaug* is very striking. The course of the story is ordained from the beginning, and the narrator deals with just those incidents which make a well-knit tale. Although our story is related to the *Saga of Egil*, it constitutes a full biography in itself, begun and rounded off with a completeness which we do not often find in the sagas. It is this unity and this insistence on love that has made some scholars question the origin of the saga.

Gunnlaug himself was a real person. He is named in the *Roll of Poets*[2] as having served Óláf the Swede, Earl Eric, and Ethelred. Four lines of Gunnlaug's poetry are quoted in Snorri's *Prose Edda*.[3]

The introduction to a translation is not the place for an attempt at an exhaustive treatment of all the problems connected with this saga. I shall content myself with a few brief references to the main problems. For a thorough discussion of the whole question of the *Saga of Gunnlaug* the reader should consult the introduction and notes to Nordal and Jónsson's edition.

Put briefly, the main problems we meet are these: the fiction surrounding several characters in the saga, errors in

3

chronology, the origin of some of the verses, and the extent of the indebtedness of this saga to other Icelandic sagas and perhaps to stories outside Iceland.

Nobody has yet been able to identify satisfactorily the Helga of this saga.[4] Her birth is as mysterious as her death. The verses give us little concrete evidence about her. Although she is named, she remains as nebulous as the loves of the Elizabethan sonneteers. There is no record outside this saga of the name of her second husband, and the children of her second marriage are not named elsewhere. Hrafn had a sister whose name was Helga,[5] and it may be that she was originally the cause of a quarrel between the two poets.[6] Perhaps Hrafn prevented the marriage of his sister, Helga, and Gunnlaug because of Gunnlaug's insult to his own poetic abilities. Gunnlaug would no doubt take such a refusal of an equal match as a slight. It may be that some two hundred years later someone saw here the germ of a tale of tragic love and rivalry and made Helga the wife and not the sister of Hrafn. Those kinsmen of Hrafn who accompany him to the last fight with Gunnlaug are not named elsewhere. The kinsmen of Ǫnund who are manhandled by Illugi are not known outside this saga.

The narrator has confused certain dates, and this may have been done deliberately. An event claimed to have taken place in the time of the life of historical figures wins some belief by a process of association. Knút, for example, did not become King of Denmark until after Gunnlaug's death, though we are told that he was king while Gunnlaug was still alive.

There is considerable doubt about the authenticity of the verses. We know that one, at least, is attributed to another poet besides Gunnlaug.[7] It seems strange that the verse attributed to Thórd, son of Kolbein, is nowhere else recorded. It is strange, too, that the important verses which caused the poets to quarrel are not recorded. We know so little of the poetry of either Gunnlaug or Hrafn, that we cannot say that the verses are really theirs.

Resemblances between this saga and other Icelandic sagas are fairly numerous. It may be that our saga borrowed its theme of love and its dream from earlier sagas. The intro-

4

duction of romance into Iceland was probably due in part to foreign influences, and it may be that the love element was derived from a foreign source, perhaps from an Irish source.[8]

All these factors, together with those mentioned in the second paragraph of this introduction, have caused much discussion about the authenticity of the *Saga of Gunnlaug*. But whether the saga is completely historical or not, it is a fine saga and exhibits most of those features which we have come to associate with the art of prose narrative at its best in medieval Europe.

Although the saga was first told orally early in the eleventh century, we have no written version of it until much later. It has come down to us in two manuscripts: one from the middle of the fourteenth century, the other from the middle of the fifteenth century. My translation is based on a collation of the variant readings of these two manuscripts as they are given in Volume III of *Íslenzk Fornrit* edited by S. Nordal and G. Jónsson, Íslenzka Fornritafélag, Reykjavik, 1938 (AM557, 4 to: University Library, Copenhagen; Sth 18 4 to: Royal Library, Stockholm).

Many English translations of the Icelandic sagas have been written in a language which is neither Modern English nor Old Icelandic. Old Icelandic was a highly inflected language, Modern English is not. Those translators who have tried to turn Modern English back into an inflected language, using words long forgotten to try to keep what they call "the spirit of the original" in their translations, create utter confusion. It is wrong to suggest in a translation that the saga audiences heard a language which seemed to them archaic and clumsy. The language of the sagas was the current language of the day, and it seems to me that a translation must also be, as far as possible, in the current language of its own day. A translation always loses something, but the "spirit" of the sagas lies as much in their narrative skill as it does in their easy, conversational style.

In dealing with the names of places, I have either translated that element of the name which will show the reader the type of place referred to or I have interpolated such a phrase as, for example, "the river" before the Icelandic name. For example: I have translated Öxará (the river of the Axe) as "the river Öx" or as "the river called Öxará." In dealing with personal names, I have generally removed the inflected element; for example: Gunnlaugr becomes Gunnlaug.

It is difficult to translate Icelandic skaldic verses. They depended for their effect mainly on two qualities. They had an elaborate use of metaphors and a complicated meter with a highly involved sentence structure. The sentence structure cannot be imitated, because English depends on word order. I have tried to avoid any suggestion of archaism in my prose, and I felt that a literal translation of the verses would probably lead not only to archaisms but also to a certain artificiality, although it is true that the language of the skaldic verses was not that of everyday. My verses are merely rhymes, and they do little justice to the originals.

There are some interesting translations of Gunnlaug's verses in *The Skalds* by Lee M. Hollander, published for The American-Scandinavian Foundation by Princeton University Press, 1947.

To a modern reader the Old Icelandic custom of "uttering a verse" on every possible occasion may seem very strange. We must remember, however, that it was in these complicated verses that Icelanders not only showed their skill, but were also able to make admissions of love, grief, anger, which would have been considered unmanly in ordinary speech.

The title, *A Poet's Love*, and the headings of the various chapters are not from the MSS.

It would be impossible for me to acknowledge all the help I have received in preparing this translation, but there are some names I feel I must mention. I owe a great debt to Professor Bruce Dickins, Corpus Christi College, Cambridge, who taught me Old Icelandic and first guided me through the *Saga of Gunnlaug*. Any merits in the translation are mainly due to his able instruction; any defects are the result of my own shortcomings. Miss Hamilton of the University of Alberta's Reference Library was always ready to procure books of reference. Dr. H. G. Leach, American-Scandinavian Foundation, has shown unfailing kindness during the various stages in the publication of my manuscript, and Professor Margaret Schlauch gave me valuable help with the translation, the introduction, and notes.

* * *

Editions of *Gunnlaugs saga*: F. Jónsson, Copenhagen, 1916; G. Jónsson, Reykjavik, 1934; L. M. Small, Leeds, 1935; S. Nordal and G. Jónsson, Reykjavik, 1938.

The edition by L. M. Small contains a fine introduction and very full notes to which I am much indebted. The edition by Nordal and Jónsson has a very full introduction and notes and some excellent prose translations of the verses in Modern Icelandic.

M. H. SCARGILL

University of Alberta

The Saga of Gunnlaug and Hrafn

1. THE FAMILY OF THORSTEIN, EGIL'S SON

THERE was a man called Thorstein. His father was Egil, son of Skalla-Grím, son of Kveldúlf, a chieftain from Norway. Thorstein's mother was called Ásgerd, and she was Bjǫrn's daughter. Thorstein lived at Borg in Borgarfjord. He was a wealthy man and an important chieftain, intelligent, calm, and a just man in every respect. He was not so valiant a man as Egil, his father, in growth or strength, and yet he was one of the most outstanding and respected men in all the nation. Thorstein was a handsome man, fair-haired, with very fine eyes. He married Jófríd, daughter of Gunnar, son of Hlíf. She had been married before to Thórodd, son of Tungu-Odd, and their daughter was Húngerd, who was brought up at Borg by Thorstein. Jófríd was a notable woman. She and Thorstein had many children, but few of them have to do with this saga. Their eldest son was Skúli, the second was Kollsvein, and the third was Egil.

2. THORSTEIN DREAMS OF A DAUGHTER

IT IS said that one summer a ship put in from the sea at the mouth of the Gufá. The skipper was called Bergfinn, a Norwegian by family, wealthy, rather old, and a man of considerable wisdom. Thorstein, the farmer, rode to the ship, for he always had the say in deciding market prices, and this occasion was no exception. The Norwegians took lodgings, and Thorstein gave hospitality to the skipper at his own request. Bergfinn was a man of few words during the course of the winter, but Thorstein made him very welcome. The Norwegian took great pleasure in interpreting dreams.

One day in the spring, Thorstein asked Bergfinn if he

8

"THORSTEIN'S DREAM"

would ride with him up under Valfell, where the people of Borgarfjord had their place of Assembly. Thorstein had heard that the walls of his booth were fallen in. The Norwegian said that he would certainly go with him, and at dawn the two of them rode off, taking one of Thorstein's servants with them. They went on until they came up under Valfell to the farmstead which is called At Grenjar.[9] Here lived a poor man whose name was Atli, one of Thorstein's tenants. Thorstein asked Atli to help them in the work and to get a hoe and a spade. Atli did as he was told. And when they came up to the walls of the booth, then all of them set to work and cleared out the walls. The weather was hot with the sun, and Thorstein and the Norwegian felt the strain of it. And when they had cleared out the walls of the booth, Thorstein and Bergfinn sat down there, and Thorstein slept and was uneasy in his sleep. The Norwegian, who sat beside him, didn't break his dreaming; but when Thorstein awoke, he was greatly distressed. The Norwegian asked him what he had been dreaming about, as he had been so uneasy in his sleep.

Thorstein said, "There is no meaning in dreams."

When they rode home in the evening, Bergfinn questioned Thorstein further about his dream, and Thorstein said, "If I do tell you the dream, then you must interpret it just as it will happen."

The Norwegian replied that they might risk that, and Thorstein went on: "I dreamed that I was at home, at Borg, and I was standing outside the men's doors of my house. Up on the house, there on the ridges, I saw a lone swan, beautiful and fair. And it seemed that I had this swan as my own, and that pleased me a good deal. Then I saw a great eagle fly down from the fells, and he flew towards the house and settled by the swan and talked with her joyfully. It seemed to me that the swan was well pleased. I saw then that the eagle was black-eyed and had iron claws; he seemed to me of noble bearing. Then I saw a second bird wing his way from the south; he flew hither to Borg and settled by the swan and wished to woo her; this one also was a great eagle. Soon it seemed to me that the eagle which flew there first grew very angry when the other one came up, and they fought together fiercely and for a long time. I saw that both of them were bleeding, and their contest ended when each of them fell dead from his side of the ridges of the house. But the swan sat on alone, downcast and sad. Then I saw a bird fly from the west, and this one was a falcon. The falcon settled by the swan and was friendly with her. Then they both flew away together in the same direction. And so I awoke."

"But this dream has no significance at all," said Thorstein, "and probably it means that storms will come together in the sky from those directions whence the birds seemed to be flying."

"It isn't my opinion that it should be so," replied the Norwegian.

"Then make of the dream what seems most probable to you," answered Thorstein, "and let me hear it."

The Norwegian said, "These birds must be the spirits[10] of men. Moreover, your wife is pregnant, and she will bear a fair and beautiful girl for whom you will have great love. Noble suitors will come to seek the hand of your daughter, and they will come from those directions whence the eagles seemed to you to fly. They will offer burning love to your daughter and they will fight for her, and this will be the death of them both. Then a third man will seek her hand, and he will come from that direction whence the falcon flew, and to him your daughter will be married. That's my interpretation of your dream, and I think it will go as I say."[11]

"The dream is explained both badly and in an unfriendly way," said Thorstein. "You can't interpret dreams at all."

"You'll find out for yourself that it will go this way," retorted the Norwegian.

Thorstein showed a certain coldness towards Bergfinn, and the Norwegian went away in the summer and is now out of our saga.

3. THE BIRTH OF HELGA

IN THE course of the summer Thorstein got ready to go to the meeting of the Assembly. Before he left home, he said to his wife, Jófríd, "It so happens that you are with child. If you bear a girl, you must expose it; but if the child is a boy, you shall rear him." For there was then a certain custom, when the land was all pagan, that those men who had few possessions, but yet had many dependents on their hands, had their children exposed.[12] And this was done in spite of the fact that the practice was always considered an evil one.

And when Thorstein had spoken thus, Jófríd replied, "This is said in a manner unworthy of such a man as you. It will be by no means seemly for a wealthy man like you to have that done."

"You know my temper," said Thorstein. "Things don't go well if it's aroused."

And then Thorstein rode off to the Assembly.

Now in Thorstein's absence Jófríd gave birth to a girl who was exceedingly fair. The women wanted to take the child from her, but Jófríd said there was little need of that. And she had her shepherd summoned and said to him, "Thorvard, you must take my horse and saddle it, and then you must carry this child westward to Thorgerd, Egil's daughter, in Hjardarholt. Ask her to bring the child up in secret, so that Thorstein won't know about it. I have such love for the child that certainly I don't intend it to be exposed. Here are three silver marks for your wages. Thorgerd must get you a passage west there and give you provision for the voyage."

Thorvard did as she said, and he rode with the child westward to Hjardarholt and gave it to Thorgerd. She had the girl brought up by some tenants who lived at Leysingjastead in Hvammsfjord. And Thorgerd got the shepherd a passage north in a ship in the bay called Skeljavik, in Steingrímsfjord. Thorvard then went abroad, and he is now out of our saga.

And when Thorstein came home from the Assembly, Jófríd told him that the child had been exposed according to his order, but that the shepherd had run away and had stolen her horse.

Thorstein said that she had done well, and he got himself another shepherd.

Now there passed six years during which the affair remained secret. And then Thorstein himself rode westward to a feast in Hjardarholt. He went to his kinsman, Óláf Peacock, who was then reckoned to be the most worthy of all the chief-

tains in the west. Thorstein was well received there, as might
be expected.

It is said that one day at the feast Thorgerd sat on a high-
seat talking to her brother Thorstein.[18] Óláf was in conversation with some other men. Opposite the two, on the benches,
there sat three maidens. Then Thorgerd asked, "How do you
like these girls, brother, who are sitting here opposite us?"

"Very well," replied Thorstein, "though one of them is by
far the prettiest. Yet, though she has the beauty of Óláf, she
has also got the fair complexion and countenance of us Mýra-
folk."

Thorgerd answered, "What you say, brother, is true
enough. She does have the complexion and the look of us
Mýra-folk, but the beauty of Óláf she has not, because she
isn't his daughter."

"How can that be, if she is your daughter?" said Thorstein.

"To tell you the truth, kinsman," said Thorgerd, "this fair
maid is your own daughter and not mine." And then she told
him everything, just as it had taken place, and she begged
him to forgive her and his wife for this offence.

"I can't reproach you two in this," said Thorstein. "Fate
goes as it will in most cases. But the pair of you have certainly remedied my lack of forethought. It strikes me this way
about the girl: I seem to have great luck in possessing so fair
a child. But what is her name?"

"She is called Helga," Thorgerd replied.

"Aye, Helga the Fair," said Thorstein. "Now you shall
get her ready to go home with me."

And Thorgerd did this. Then Thorstein was conducted
thence with good gifts, and Helga rode home with him. She
grew up at Borg with great honour and love from her father
and mother and from all her kinsfolk.

4. GUNNLAUG AND HELGA:
FIRST MEETING

AT THIS time there dwelt up on the bank of the river called
Hvítá, at Gilsbank, Illugi the Black, son of Hallkell who was

the son of Hrosskell. The mother of Illugi was Thuríd Sow-thistle, daughter of Gunnlaug Serpent's Tongue. Illugi was the next greatest chieftain to Thorstein, Egil's son, in Bor-garfjord. He was a great landowner, very hard to deal with—though he gave plenty of help to his friends. He married Ingibjǫrg, daughter of Ásbjǫrn Hardarson from Ǫrnólfs-dale. The mother of Ingibjǫrg was Thorgerd, the daughter of Skegg of Midfjord. The children of Ingibjǫrg and Illugi were many, but few of them have to do with this saga. Her-mund was the name of one son, and another was called Gunn-laug. Both of them were promising lads and in their prime.

It is said of Gunnlaug that he grew mature at an early age.[14] He was tall and strong and had light-chestnut hair that suited him very well. He had black eyes, a somewhat ugly nose, but he was well shaped in the face, slender in the waist and broad-shouldered. He was the most accomplished of men, most self-assertive in his whole disposition; from an early age he was eager and headstrong in everything. He was a bold fellow and a great poet, though rather libellous—hence his name Gunnlaug Serpent's Tongue.

Hermund, who had the bearing of a chieftain, was the more popular of the two.

And when Gunnlaug was twelve years old, he asked his father for equipment for a journey, saying that he wanted to go abroad and see how other men lived.

Illugi heard this request with some reluctance, and he said that Gunnlaug would hardly get a good name abroad, when he seemed scarcely able to control himself at home as his father wished.

But it happened one morning a little later that Illugi went out early and saw that his store-house was open and that some six sacks of homespun, the saddle-pads with them, were laid out on the pavement. Illugi was greatly surprised at this. Then a man came there and led out four horses. And this turned out to be his son Gunnlaug, who said, "I have laid out the sacks."

Illugi asked him why he had done this, and Gunnlaug re-plied that this was to be his equipment for traveling.

"You won't get my consent," said Illugi. "You will go

14

nowhere, before I desire it." And he slung the sacks in again.

Then Gunnlaug rode away, and in the evening he came down to Borg, and Thorstein asked him to stay there. Gunnlaug accepted, and he told Thorstein how it had gone between him and his father. Thorstein invited Gunnlaug to stay with him as long as he wished, and he did remain with them all the year, studying law under Thorstein. He became very popular with everyone.

Helga and Gunnlaug, who were of an age, were always playing chess together, and each seemed at once agreeable to the other—as indeed it came out later.

Helga was so beautiful that those who know said that she was the loveliest woman there has ever been in Iceland. Her hair was of such a length that it could cover her entirely, and it was as fair as beaten gold. There did not seem so good a choice as Helga the Fair in all Borgarfjord or farther afield.

On a certain day, when the men sat in the sitting-room at Borg, Gunnlaug said to Thorstein, "There is one part of the law which you haven't taught me, and that is how to betroth myself."

"That's a small matter," said Thorstein, and he taught him the procedure.

Then Gunnlaug said, "Now you shall know if I have understood. I will take your hand and behave as if I were betrothing myself to your daughter Helga."

"I think there is little need of that," said Thorstein.

Then Gunnlaug seized his hand and said, "Grant me this now."

"Do as you wish," said Thorstein. "But let all present know that this shall be as if unspoken and that no secret stipulation shall accompany it."

So Gunnlaug named his witnesses, and he betrothed himself to Helga. Then he asked if this might stand.

Thorstein said that it could be valid, and at this there was great pleasure among the men who were present.

5. THE FAMILY OF HRAFN. HOW HELGA WAS PROMISED TO GUNNLAUG

THERE was a man called Qnund, and he lived in the south at Mosfell. Qnund was very wealthy and held the priesthood there on the southern headland. He was married, and his wife was called Geirný. She was the daughter of Gnúp, son of that Molda-Gnúp who settled in Grindavík in the south. Their sons were Hrafn, Thorarin, and Eindrid. They were all promising men, but Hrafn surpassed the others in every respect. He was a tall, strong man, very handsome, and a good poet. When Hrafn was come to manhood, he went out trading and was well liked wherever he went. In the south at Hjalli in Qlfus there lived Thórodd the Wise, the son of Eyvind, and Skapti, his son, who was then Law-speaker in Iceland. Skapti's mother was Rannveig, daughter of Gnúp, son of Molda-Gnúp; and the sons of Skapti and of Qnund were cousins, and there was great friendship between them. At that time there lived at Rauthmel Thorfinn, the son of Sel-Thórir, and he had seven sons and they were all promising men. The names of Thorfinn's sons were Thorgils, Eyjólf, and Thórir, and they were then the greatest men in those parts. And these men whom we have named were all living at the same time.

And about this time befell those tidings, the best that have ever been here in Iceland, that the country had become entirely Christian and all the people had forsaken the old faith.[15]

And now for six years, as previously told, Gunnlaug was either at Borg with Thorstein or at Gilsbank with his father Illugi. By this time he was eighteen years old, and father and son were much alike in mind.

There was a man called Thorkell the Black, one of Illugi's household, a near kinsman, and one who had grown up at Gilsbank. An inheritance had fallen to Thorkell, and it was up north in Vatnsdale in Ás. Thorkell asked Gunnlaug to go there with him, and Gunnlaug did so. The two of them rode together north into Ás, and they took over the property from those to whom it had been entrusted, and Gunnlaug acted as executor.

16

When they rode up north, they passed the night in Gríms-tunga with a wealthy farmer who lived there. In the morning a shepherd took out Gunnlaug's horse, and when they got it back, it was in a great sweat. Gunnlaug knocked the shepherd senseless. The farmer didn't like things that way, and he demanded compensation for it. Gunnlaug offered to pay him a mark, but he thought that was too little. Then Gunnlaug spoke this verse:

1. Come now, farmer, take this fee
   For thy servant stricken low,
   Or thou shalt find thy scorn of me
   Side by side with sorrow go.

The affair was settled in accordance with Gunnlaug's offer, and they rode home with matters thus concluded.

A little later Gunnlaug asked his father a second time for equipment for a journey.

"This time it shall be as you wish," Illugi replied, "for you are now much improved from what you were."

Illugi then rode quickly from home, and on Gunnlaug's behalf he bargained with Audun Cable-hound[16] for half interest in a ship which stood at the mouth of the Gufá. This was that same Audun who refused to give passage abroad to the sons of Ósvíf the Wise after the manslaughter of Kjartan, son of Óláf, as it is told in Laxdale Saga, but that was later than this.

And when Illugi came back home, Gunnlaug thanked him.

Thorkell the Black resolved to make the journey abroad with Gunnlaug, and their goods were conveyed to the ship. Gunnlaug remained at Borg whilst they fitted out the vessel, and he seemed more pleased to be in speech with Helga than to be at business with the merchants.

One day Thorstein asked Gunnlaug if he would like to ride with him up to the horses in Langavatnsdale, and Gunnlaug agreed. So the two of them rode together until they reached the stables belonging to Thorstein which were called At Thorgilsstead. There were the horses which Thorstein possessed, and they were four in number and of a red colour. One stallion was very promising, but little proved, and Thor-

stein offered to give it to Gunnlaug. But he said that he had
no need of horses, since he intended to leave the country.
Then they rode on to some other horses, and there was a grey
stallion with four mares. The stallion was the best in Borgarfjord, and Thorstein offered to give it to Gunnlaug.

"I will have neither this horse nor that one," said Gunnlaug. "But why don't you offer me that which I will accept?"

"And what is that?" asked Thorstein.

"Your daughter, Helga the Fair," replied Gunnlaug.

"That can't be settled so easily," said Thorstein, and he
took up another topic.

And so they rode homewards down the bank of the river
called Langá.

Then Gunnlaug said, "I'd like to know what answer you
intend to give to my request."

"I'm paying no attention to your idle talk," replied Thorstein.

"This is no idle talk," answered Gunnlaug. "I am in real
earnest."

Thorstein replied, "First of all, you'd better make up your
mind about what you want. Aren't you settled upon going
abroad? And yet you behave as if you wanted to get married.
It isn't an equal match between Helga and you whilst you
are so unsettled. The matter can't be considered."

"And where do you reckon there is a fit match for your
daughter if you won't give her to the son of Illugi the Black?"
asked Gunnlaug. "Where are those in Borgarfjord who are of
greater importance than my father?"

Thorstein replied, "I am not entering into a comparison of
men. If you were a man like your father, then you wouldn't
be rejected."

"To whom would you rather give your daughter than to
me?" asked Gunnlaug.

"There is no lack in choice of good men here," replied
Thorstein. "There's Thorfinn at Rauthmel has seven sons,
and they are all of them well brought up."

Gunnlaug said, "Neither Thorfinn nor even Onund[17] himself is an equal match for my father, because you are clearly
his inferior. And what do you have to set against the fact

18

that my father had a contest with Thórgrim the Priest, Kjal-
lak's son, at the Assembly at Thórness, and his sons with him,
and alone my father had his own way?"

"I myself drove away Steinar, son of Qnund Sjóni," replied Thorstein, "and that was reckoned a feat of no small
importance."

"You had your father, Egil,[18] to thank for that," said
Gunnlaug. "And, to end this, it would turn out well for few
farmers to refuse kinship by marriage with me."

"Keep your threats for those upon the Fell," answered
Thorstein, "for they won't serve you here in the Marshes."

And in the evening they reached home.

In the morning Gunnlaug rode off to Gilsbank, and he
asked his father to ride with him to a wooing out at Borg.

"You are an unsettled fellow," replied Illugi, "for you have
arranged to go abroad, but now you carry on as if you were
going to be busy getting married. I know that this won't suit
Thorstein's temper."

"I intend to go abroad all the same," replied Gunnlaug.
"And I shall not be pleased, unless you pursue this."

Then Illugi, with eleven men, rode from home to Borg, and
Thorstein received him well.

Early in the morning Illugi said to Thorstein, "I would
like to have a talk with you."

"Let us go up to the top of Borg and talk there," replied
Thorstein.[19] And they did this, and Gunnlaug went with them.

Then Illugi said, "My son, Gunnlaug, says that he has
broached to you a proposal on his own behalf for the hand
of your daughter Helga. Now I should like to know how the
matter is to stand. You know his family and our wealth. I
shall spare nothing on our side in the way of dwelling and
servants, if that makes it more likely than before."

Thorstein replied, "I have only this one thing against
Gunnlaug, that he seems to me to be unsettled. If he had your
disposition, then I should make little delay."

Illugi answered, "If you refuse an equal match in my son
and me, it will cause a breach of friendship between us two."

Then said Thorstein, "Because of your words and our

own friendship, Helga shall be promised, but not yet betrothed,[20] to Gunnlaug. And they must wait three years. Gunnlaug must go abroad and conduct himself as noble men do. If he doesn't come back in that time or if his character doesn't please me, I shall be free from all promises."

And they parted with things settled thus. Illugi rode home, and Gunnlaug went to his ship.

And when they got a fair wind they put out to sea and went north with their vessel to Norway. They sailed into Thrándheim into the mouth of the river Nid, and there they weighed anchor and unloaded.

6. GUNNLAUG ANGERS EARL ERIC

AND at that time Earl Eric, the son of Hákon, ruled in Norway with his brother Svein. Eric was then living in his patrimony at Hladir, and he was a powerful chieftain.

Skúli, Thorstein's son, was then with the Earl. He was a retainer and highly valued.

They say that Gunnlaug and Audun Cable-hound went with ten others to Hladir and that Gunnlaug was dressed in a grey tunic and white breeches. He had a boil under his foot on the instep, and when he walked, it frothed up with blood and oozed out pus. And in such condition he and Audun and party went before the Earl, and they greeted him well. The Earl knew Audun, and he asked him the news from Iceland. Audun gave him such news as there was. The Earl asked Gunnlaug who he might be, and Gunnlaug told him his name and kinship.

Then the Earl said "Skúli, what kind of man is this in Iceland?"

"Sire, receive him well," replied Skúli, "for he is the son of the best man in Iceland, Illugi the Black, from Gilsbank, who is my foster-brother."

"What is the matter with your foot, Icelander?" asked the Earl.

"There is a boil on it, Sire," Gunnlaug replied.

"Yet you didn't limp," said the Earl.

"I shall not go lame whilst both my legs are of the same length," replied Gunnlaug.

Then said one of the Earl's retainers, Thórir by name, "This fellow is behaving arrogantly, this Icelander. It would be a good thing if we were to test him somewhat."

Gunnlaug looked at him and said:

> 2. Mistrust yon retainer,
> So swarthy and vile;
> None is more crafty,
> Deep-fanged with guile.

Then Thórir would have gripped his axe, but the Earl said, "Let it be. Men should pay no attention to such nonsense. How old are you, Icelander?"

Gunnlaug replied, "I am now eighteen."

"I dare solemnly vow," said the Earl, "that you won't see another eighteen years."

Gunnlaug replied in a rather low voice. "Wish me no evil, but rather wish good for yourself."

"What are you saying now, Icelander?" asked the Earl.

Gunnlaug answered, "I was saying that I think you should not pray evil for me, but you should rather make more useful requests on your own behalf."

"What about?" asked the Earl.

"That you don't meet such a death as did your father, Earl Hákon,"[21] replied Gunnlaug.

The Earl went red as blood, and he bade them seize the fool with speed.

But then Skúli went before the Earl and said, "Sire, grant my request and keep peace with him and let him depart as soon as possible."

The Earl answered, "Let him be off as soon as he can, if he wants peace, and let him never come within my kingdom again."

Then Skúli went out with Gunnlaug and down to the quays. There was a ship bound for England, quite ready to put to sea, and Skúli got a passage on it for Gunnlaug and Thorkell, his kinsman. Gunnlaug handed over his ship into the custody of Audun and did the same with those of his goods which he didn't take with him.

And now Gunnlaug and the rest sailed into the English sea, and in autumn they came south to the port of London, and there they beached their ship.

7. GUNNLAUG WINS FAME IN ENGLAND

At that time King Ethelred, son of Edgar, ruled England, and he was a good leader.[22] He held court that winter in London.

There was then the one language in England just as in Norway and Denmark. But languages changed in England when William the Bastard won that country, and then the French language became current, for William was of French descent.

Gunnlaug went before the King at once and greeted him well and honourably.

The King asked him what land he came from, and Gunnlaug told him. "But," he said, "I have sought audience with you, Sire, because I have made a poem about you, and I would like you to hear it."

The King said that he would listen, and Gunnlaug recited his poem well and proudly:

> 3. As a god, his people
>   Hold Ethelred in dread;
>   Unto such a warlike King
>   All nations bow the head.

The King thanked Gunnlaug for the poem and, as a reward for it, gave him a scarlet cloak, lined with the finest fur and ornamented at the hem with lace. The King made Gunnlaug his retainer, and Gunnlaug remained with him throughout the winter and was valued highly.

One day early in the morning Gunnlaug met three men in a certain street. Their leader was called Thórorm, a tall, strong man, wondrously villainous-looking.

Thórorm demanded, "Northerner, lend me some money!"

Gunnlaug replied, "There is no sense in giving money to strangers."

"I will repay you upon the day appointed," said the fellow.

"Then I'll take the risk," said Gunnlaug, and he gave him the money.

Now a short time after this, Gunnlaug met the King and told him about the loan.

But the King said, "Now you have done unwisely, for this man is the greatest robber and pirate. Don't have any truck with him; I will give you an equal sum of money."

Gunnlaug replied, "Things go badly with us your retainers, if we pick a quarrel with innocent men but let such as this one bully us. That shall never be."

Soon after this Gunnlaug met Thórorm and demanded the money from him. But Thórorm said that he would not pay.

Gunnlaug then spoke these lines:

4. Thou sword-wielder, over bold,
   Red gold will withhold, foolish and vain.
   I of the Serpent's Tongue,
   Name earned when I was young,[23] may prove thy bane.

Then said Gunnlaug, "Now I will offer you a legal settlement. You shall either give me my money or you shall fight a duel with me after three days."

Then the pirate laughed, and he said, "Until this time none but you has undertaken to challenge me to a duel, though not a few have been wronged by me. I am quite ready to accept your proposal."

And with that he and Gunnlaug parted for the present.

Gunnlaug told the King that the affair was settled in that way, but the King said, "Things have now come to a very ugly situation. This fellow can turn the edge of every weapon. From now on you must act in accordance with my advice. I am going to give you this sword, and you must fight with it, but show him another one."

And Gunnlaug thanked the King well.

And when they were ready for the duel, Thórorm asked Gunnlaug what kind of sword he had. Gunnlaug drew his sword and showed it to him. But he had a loop about the middle of the King's gift and concealed it with his hand. When the berserk saw the weapon he said, "I am not afraid of that sword." And he struck at Gunnlaug with his own

sword and cut nearly all his shield from in front of him. Then
Gunnlaug struck in return with the King's gift. The berserk
stood without shield, for he thought that Gunnlaug had the
same weapon as the one he had shown. And Gunnlaug struck
him a blow which was his death at once.

The King thanked Gunnlaug for his deed, and he got great
fame from it in England and farther afield.

In the spring, when the ships went on trading voyages,
Gunnlaug asked King Ethelred for permission to sail. The
King asked what he wanted to do then, and Gunnlaug replied,
"I wish to carry out that which I have promised to do." Then
he spoke this verse:

> 5. I go to seek far-distant courts[24]
>   Of mighty Earls and Kings,
>   To prove my words of other days
>   Are no vain things.
>   So fare thee well; yet know, great King,
>   That I shall come again,
>   If thou in trouble, war or peace,
>   Dost call upon my name.

"So it shall be, poet," said the King, and he gave Gunnlaug
a ring weighing six ounces in pure gold. "But you must
promise me to return next autumn, for I don't want to let you
go because of your great skill."

8. HOW GUNNLAUG WON ERIC'S FAVOUR AGAIN

THEN Gunnlaug sailed from England with merchants north
to Dublin. At that time King Sigtrygg Silken-beard[25] ruled in
Ireland, and he was the son of Óláf Kváran and Queen
Kormlad. Sigtrygg had then ruled in his kingdom but a
short time. Gunnlaug went before the King and greeted him
well and respectfully, and the King received him honourably.

Gunnlaug said, "I have made a poem about you, and I
would like to get a hearing for it."

"Until this time men have not brought me a poem," said
the King, "and I shall certainly hear it."

Gunnlaug recited the poem, and this is the refrain:

6. Sigtrygg feeds the wolf with carrion.[26]

And this is part of the poem:

7. Hail Kváran's son! I hymn thee;
   King-born, great praise I bring thee.
   Thou friend of poet, noble lord,
   Generous giver, hear my word!

8. Let the King say if greater praise
   Has touched his ear in others' lays.

The King thanked Gunnlaug for the poem, then he called to his treasurer and asked, "How shall I reward it?"

"How do you wish to reward it, Sire?" asked the treasurer.

"What kind of a reward is it if I give him two ships?"

"That is too much, Sire," replied the treasurer. "As a reward for a poem other Kings give noble treasures, such as fine swords or costly golden rings."

The King gave Gunnlaug his own cloak of new scarlet, a laced tunic, a cloak lined with fine furs, and a gold ring that weighed a mark. And Gunnlaug thanked him well, and he remained there for a short time. Then he went from Ireland to the Orkneys.

Earl Sigurd,[27] son of Hladvir, ruled in the Orkneys, and he was well disposed towards Icelanders. Gunnlaug greeted him well and said that he had a poem to recite for him.

The Earl said that he would hear the poem, since Gunnlaug came of such great kindred in Iceland. Gunnlaug recited the poem, and it was a short lay and well composed.

The Earl gave him a broad axe all plated with silver as a reward for the poem, and he invited Gunnlaug to remain with him. Gunnlaug thanked him for the gift and the invitation, but he said that he was on his way east to Sweden. And later he went on board ship with some merchants who were sailing for Norway, and in the autumn they came east to Konungahella. And Thorkell, his kinsman, accompanied Gunnlaug all this time.

From Konungahella they got a guide up into West Gotland, and they came into a market-town called Skarir. There

ruled that Earl who was called Sigurd, and he was very old. Gunnlaug went before him and greeted him well and told him that he had made a poem about him. The Earl was very ready to hear it. And Gunnlaug recited his poem, and it was a short lay. The Earl thanked him and rewarded him well, and he invited Gunnlaug to stay with him during the winter.

Earl Sigurd had a great Yule banquet in the winter, and on Christmas Eve there came north from Norway messengers of Earl Eric, twelve of them together, and they brought gifts for Earl Sigurd. The Earl received them well and assigned them seats by Gunnlaug for the Yule season. And there was great merriment and ale-drinking.

The Geats boasted that no Earl was greater or more famous than Sigurd. But to the Norwegians Earl Eric seemed far more distinguished. They grew angry about this and called on Gunnlaug as arbitrator between both sides in the dispute. Gunnlaug then spoke this verse:

> 9. Warriors, you have told me
> Of this aged Earl
> That he has seen the mighty waves
> Before his vessel swirl.
> True is that; yet, Eric, too,
> Has crossed the heaving main
> And from the prow of speeding ship
> Has heard the east sea strain.

Both sides were pleased with the decision, especially the Norwegians. And after Yule the messengers went thence with gifts of money which Sigurd sent to Earl Eric. And now they told Earl Eric about Gunnlaug's decision. It seemed to the Earl that Gunnlaug had shown fairness and friendship, and he let it be known that Gunnlaug should have a place of retreat in his kingdom. Gunnlaug heard later what the Earl had decided.

And now Earl Sigurd gave Gunnlaug a guide east into Tiundaland,[28] in Sweden, as he requested.

9. GUNNLAUG AND HRAFN MEET IN FRIENDSHIP BUT THEY PART IN WRATH

AT THAT time King Óláf the Swede ruled over the Swedish folk. He was the son of King Eric the Victorious and Sigríd the Haughty,[29] daughter of Tósti the Warrior. Óláf was a powerful and famous King, a man of great ambition.

Gunnlaug came to Upsala near the time of the Assembly of the Swedes in the spring,[30] and when he obtained a meeting with the King, he greeted him. The King received him well and asked who he was. Gunnlaug replied that he was an Icelander.

Now at that time Hrafn, the son of Qnund, was in Óláf's company, and the King said to him, "Hrafn, tell me what kind of man this is in Iceland."

And a man stood up from one of the lower benches, and he was tall and of brave bearing. He went before the King and said, "Sire, he is a most valiant man himself and is of the best family."

"Let him go then and sit by you," said the King.

Gunnlaug said, "I have a poem to recite to you, and I would like you to give it a hearing and to listen to it."

"Go first and sit you both down," said the King, "for there is no leisure time now to spend sitting over verses."

And so Gunnlaug and Hrafn took their seats and talked together. Each one told the other about his travels. Hrafn said that he had journeyed in the summer before from Iceland to Norway, and at the beginning of winter he had traveled east to Sweden. The two of them soon became friendly at the court.

One day when the Assembly was done and they were both in the King's presence, Gunnlaug said, "Now, Sire, I would like you to hear my poem."

"I can do that now," said the King.

"Sire, I would like to recite my own poem now," said Hrafn.

"That's quite acceptable," replied the King.

"Then will I recite mine first, Sire," said Gunnlaug, "if you like."

27

"I have the right to be first to recite, Sire," said Hrafn, "since I was first to come to you."

But Gunnlaug said, "When did it happen that your father ever towed mine around? Never! And we'll let that example hold good for us."

Hrafn replied, "Let us behave courteously and not enter into an argument about this. We will let the King rule."

And the King said, "Gunnlaug shall recite first, for he will lose his temper if he doesn't get his own way."

Then Gunnlaug recited the poem which he had composed about King Óláf, and when the poem was ended, the King said, "Hrafn, what is your criticism of that poem?"

"Well, Sire," said he, "it is a high-sounding poem, but it is ugly and somewhat stiff in composition, just as Gunnlaug himself is in his temper."

"And now you shall recite your poem, Hrafn," said the King.

Hrafn did so, and when the poem was ended, the King asked Gunnlaug, "Now what do you think of the composition of that poem?"

Gunnlaug replied, "Well, Sire, it's a very fine verse, just as Hrafn himself is fine to see, but it is a mean one. But, Hrafn, why have you composed a short lay about a King? Didn't he seem to you worthy of a longer poem?"[31]

Hrafn replied, "Let's drop the conversation for the time being. But this will be taken up again, even though it be later on."

And then they parted with matters in that state.

A little later, when Hrafn had become a retainer of King Óláf, he asked the King's permission to journey away, and the King granted it. Now when Hrafn was ready for his journey out, he said to Gunnlaug, "Our friendship shall now be at an end, because you had it in mind to shame me here before the chieftains. Now, whenever I can, I shall shame you no less than you desired to shame me in this."

Gunnlaug replied, "Your threats don't trouble me, and we two shall never come to the point that I shall be valued less than you."

28

King Óláf gave Hrafn noble gifts when they parted, and then Hrafn went away.

Hrafn journeyed from the east in the spring and came to Thrándheim and fitted out his ship. He sailed to Iceland in the summer, and he brought his ship into the bay called Leiruvág, below Heath. His kinsmen and his friends rejoiced at his coming, and he remained at home that winter with his father.

During the summer at the Assembly Hrafn met his kinsman, Skapti the Law-speaker.[32] And Hrafn said to him, "I would like to have your help in a wooing, to ask Thorstein, Egil's son, for the hand of his daughter Helga."

But Skapti asked him, "Isn't she already betrothed to Gunnlaug Serpent's Tongue?"

Hrafn answered, "Isn't the appointed time announced for them now gone? Besides, his overbearing disposition is now so great that he won't watch this or pay any attention to it."

"Let us do as it pleases you," answered Skapti.

And then they went with many people to the booth of Thorstein, and he made them very welcome.

Skapti said to him, "My kinsman, Hrafn, wants to ask for your daughter Helga. His family is known to you, and so is his great wealth, good breeding, and the power of his kinsmen and friends."

Thorstein replied, "She is already promised to Gunnlaug, and I intend to keep with him the whole agreement in those things appointed."

Skapti said, "Aren't the three years which were named between you both now passed?"

"Not till the summer is gone," said Thorstein, "and he may yet come during this summer."

"If he doesn't come during the summer," said Skapti, "what hopes can we have from this talk?"

"We must likely come here next summer," replied Thorstein, "and then we can see what appears to be most advisable. I don't see any point in discussing this further for the present."

And with that they parted, and men rode home from the Assembly.

That conversation didn't go concealed, that Hrafn was

asking for Helga's hand. And Gunnlaug didn't come back to Iceland that summer.

At the Assembly next summer Skapti and his people made their request with some heat and said that Thorstein was free from all agreements with Gunnlaug.

Thorstein said, "I have few daughters to provide for, and I am anxious that they should be the cause of strife to nobody. Now I have a mind first of all to see Illugi the Black."

He went to see Illugi, and when they met he said, "Does it seem to you that I am free from all agreements with your son Gunnlaug?"

Illugi replied, "It is certainly so, if you want it that way. There is very little I can say about it, because I don't quite know how the affairs of my son Gunnlaug stand."

Thorstein then went back to Skapti, and they agreed that the wedding feast should take place during the Winter Nights at Borg, provided that Gunnlaug didn't come to Iceland during the summer. Thorstein was to be free from all agreements with Hrafn, if Gunnlaug should arrive and come to fetch his bride. After that men rode home from the Assembly.

The arrival of Gunnlaug was delayed, and Helga thought that all was ill-advised.

10. HOW GUNNLAUG HEARD OF HELGA'S BETROTHAL

Now it must be said that Gunnlaug went from Sweden to England in the same summer that Hrafn sailed to Iceland, and he received fine gifts from King Óláf when they parted.

King Ethelred received Gunnlaug very well, and Gunnlaug spent the winter with him in great honour. At that time Canute the Powerful, the son of Svein, ruled over Denmark, and he had newly acquired his patrimony. He was always vowing to harry England, because his father had won great territory in England before he died in the west there. And at that time there was a great host of Danes there in the west, and their chieftain was called Heming. He was the son of Earl Strút-Harald and brother of Earl Sigvald, and he held from

King Canute that land which King Svein had formerly won.

In the spring, Gunnlaug asked the King's permission to leave. Ethelred replied "Since you are my retainer, it is not fitting that you should leave me now, in face of such hostilities as are ahead of us in England."

Gunnlaug said, "You shall command me, Sire; but give me permission to go away in the summer, if the Danes don't come."

The King said, "We shall see when the time comes."

Now that summer passed and winter after it, but the Danes did not come. And after midsummer Gunnlaug got the King's permission to go away, and then he went eastwards to Norway, and met Earl Eric in Thrándheim, at Hladir, and the Earl gave him a good welcome and invited him to stay with him. Gunnlaug thanked him for the invitation, but said that he wanted to go to Iceland first to claim his betrothed.

Earl Eric said "All the ships bound for Iceland have gone."

Then a retainer said, "Hallfred Troublesome Poet[33] lay at anchor yesterday way out under Agdaness."

The Earl replied, "It may be so, for he sailed hence five days ago."

Earl Eric then had Gunnlaug taken out to Hallfred, and he received him hospitably. Straight away they got a fair wind from the land, and they were very merry. That was late in the summer. And Hallfred asked Gunnlaug, "Have you heard about the courtship of Hrafn, son of Qnund, and Helga the Fair?" Gunnlaug said he had heard, but not very fully. Hallfred told him what he knew about it and said also that many men reckoned that Hrafn would prove no less brave than Gunnlaug.

Gunnlaug then spoke this verse:

> 10. Let the howling east-wind
> Lash the waves to foam,
> Break this landsman's weather,
> Drive our vessel home.
> Let it bear my threat to Hrafn,
> And shout where'er he be,
> He shall not be an equal
> Till death tries grips with me.

Then said Hallfred, "Friend, you'll need to have a more satisfactory meeting with Hrafn than I did. I brought my ship into Leiruvag, below Heath, a few winters ago and was supposed to pay toll of half a mark in silver to Hrafn's servant, but I withheld it from him. Up came Hrafn to us with sixty men, and they cut our cable and pushed the ship out on to the mud flats and wrecked us. Then had I to pay Hrafn what he wanted to ask, and so I handed over a mark. And that's the tale of my dealings with him."

Then they talked of nothing but Helga, and Hallfred gave great praise to her beauty.

Gunnlaug then spoke this verse:

> 11. Nay, Hrafn, do not think that thou
> Canst win the white-clad Helga now.
> We in youth, quick-loving both,
> Did join our hands to seal our troth.

"That's a well-composed verse," said Hallfred.

Gunnlaug and Hallfred reached land up north by the plain called Melrakkasletta, in Hraunhaven, two weeks before winter, and there they unloaded.

Now there was a man called Thord, a farmer's son, there at Sletta. He took up wrestling matches with the merchants, and they had a bad time of it against him. A match was arranged between Thord and Gunnlaug, and on the night before they met Thord called upon Thór for victory. Next day, when they met and began to wrestle, Gunnlaug got both feet from under Thord and brought him down very heavily. But the foot on which Gunnlaug bore his weight went out of joint, so that he fell down together with Thord.

Then said Thord, "It may be that something else won't go any better with you either."

"And what might that be?" asked Gunnlaug.

"Your meeting with Hrafn, if he weds Helga the Fair at the Winter Nights. I was there at the Assembly in the summer when that was arranged."

Gunnlaug made no reply. Then his foot was bound up and set in joint again, but it swelled a good deal.

Gunnlaug and Hallfred, in company with ten men, rode off, and they came south to Gilsbank in Borgarfjord on the very Saturday evening when folks sat at the wedding feast at Borg. Illugi was glad to see Gunnlaug and his fellow travelers. Gunnlaug said that he wanted to ride down to Borg at once, but Illugi said that wasn't advisable, and so it seemed to everybody except Gunnlaug. Gunnlaug was then disabled because of his foot, though he didn't let that be seen. So there was no journey made.

Next day Hallfred rode home to Hreiduwater[34] in Nordrár- dale. Galti, his brother, looked after the property which they both shared there, and he was a valiant man.

11. GUNNLAUG GOES TO A WEDDING. THE DUEL AT THE ASSEMBLY

Now it must be told that Hrafn sat at his wedding feast at Borg. And it is the report of most men that the bride was rather sad, for that proverb is a true one which says, "What youth doth gain the mind must needs retain." This was proved in the case of Helga then.

There was something new at the feast when the man called Sverting asked for the hand of Húngerd, daughter of Thór- odd and Jófríd. Sverting was the son of Hafr-Bjǫrn, Molda- Gnúp's son. They decided that the wedding should take place up at Skáney in the winter, after Yule. There lived Thorkell, one of Húngerd's kinsmen and the son of Torfi, Válbrand's son. Torfi's mother was Thórodda,[35] the sister of Tungu-Odd.

Now Hrafn went home to Mosfell with his wife Helga. And when they had been there a short time, it happened one morning before they got up, that Helga lay awake whilst Hrafn slept, and he had a bad dream. When he awoke, Helga asked what he had dreamed about, and Hrafn spoke this verse:

> 12. I dreamed that I lay bleeding,
> Beauteous bride;
> Life-blood welling
> From my side.

33

No staunching of wounds,
As the red rain drips;
Nay, Helga, a smile
Was on thy lips.

Helga replied, "I should never weep for that. And you have every one of you evilly betrayed me, for Gunnlaug has surely come back to Iceland." And she wept bitterly.

A short time later Gunnlaug's arrival in Iceland was reported. Helga then became so harsh towards Hrafn that he could no longer keep her at home. So back they went to Borg, and Hrafn had little pleasure from his wedded life with Helga.

Now folks began to get ready for the wedding feast in the winter, and Thorkell from Skáney invited Illugi the Black and his sons. But when Illugi was getting ready, Gunnlaug remained in the sitting-room and made no preparation at all. Illugi went to him and said, "Why aren't you getting ready, kinsman?"

Gunnlaug replied, "I have no intention of going."

"You shall certainly go, my son," said Illugi. "And don't betake yourself to yearning after a woman. Behave as if you didn't care, and you will never lack women."

So Gunnlaug did as his father wished, and they arrived at the wedding feast.

Illugi and his sons were placed on one high-seat, and Thorstein and Hrafn, his son-in-law, together with the bridegroom's company, were placed on a second high-seat opposite Illugi. The women sat on a cross bench, and Helga the Fair sat next to the bride. Helga often looked at Gunnlaug, and there was proved that proverb that says, "The eyes will betray a woman's love for a man." On that occasion Gunnlaug was finely arrayed, and he wore the cloak and goodly clothes which King Sigtrygg gave him. He seemed the greatest of all the men there for many reasons, for strength, beauty, and stature too. There was little merriment among folk at that feast.

On the day when the men were preparing for their departure, and when the women, too, set about their going and made ready for the journey home, then Gunnlaug went to talk

34

"THE SERPENT AND THE RAVEN"

to Helga. They talked for a long time together, and then Gunnlaug spoke this verse:

> 13. The sun is dark, and dark is life
>   Since Helga first was Hrafn's wife.
>   The lady's father, white and old,
>   Sold my bride to win him gold.

And he recited further:

> 14. Cursed be thy father,
>   Cursed be his skill
>   To breed a child,
>   To work me ill.
>   Them I curse, but never thee.
>   Devil take both for scorning me.

And then Gunnlaug gave Helga the cloak which was the gift of Ethelred, and it was a most costly thing. She thanked him well for the gift.

Then Gunnlaug went out, and the horses and pack-horses were come. Many of them were very promising animals, and they stood tied up on the pavement of the house. Gunnlaug jumped on the back of one horse, and he galloped over the home-meadow to where Hrafn was standing before him, and Hrafn had to draw back. But Gunnlaug said, "There is no need for you to go back, Hrafn, since I offer you no threats this time. But you know quite well what you have deserved."

Hrafn spoke this verse in reply:

> 15. To quarrel, Warrior, would work us shame,
>   To spill red blood in woman's name.
>   Take thy ship across the sea:
>   There are women as fair, it seems to me.

Gunnlaug replied, "It may be that there are many as fair as Helga, but it doesn't seem so to me."

Then Illugi and Thorstein rushed there, and they didn't want the two to quarrel. Gunnlaug then spoke this verse:

> 16. Not less in arms than me, men hold
>   Him who bought my bride with gold.
>   My journey stayed at great king's will;
>   Yet—let my tongue be still.

And after that the men took their separate directions home, and all was quiet and void of incident during the winter. But Hrafn had no relations with Helga after she and Gunnlaug had met.[36]

In the summer men rode in great numbers to the Assembly. There was Illugi the Black, and with him were his sons Gunnlaug and Hermund. Thorstein, Egil's son, and his son Kollsvein were there. Qnund from Mosfell and all his sons and Sverting, the son of Hafr-Bjǫrn, were there. And at that time Skapti still held the office of Law-speaker.

And one day at the Assembly, when men flocked in great numbers to the Law Rock, when the suits were all decided, Gunnlaug asked for a hearing and said, "Is Hrafn, the son of Qnund, here?"

Hrafn answered to his name.

And Gunnlaug then went on, "You know that you have taken my own betrothed and shown yourself no friend to me, and now, for that, I want to challenge you to a duel here at the Assembly, to be on Öxará Islet after three days' respite."

Hrafn replied, "Your offer is a fair one, as was expected from you. And I am ready to take it up, as soon as you wish."

That seemed a bad thing to the kinsmen of each of them, but yet it was legal at that time for a man who thought himself to be unfairly dealt with by another to issue a challenge. And when three days had gone, they got ready for the duel. Illugi the Black accompanied his son to the islet with a considerable following; Skapti the Law-speaker, Qnund, and other kinsmen, went out with Hrafn. And before Gunnlaug went out on to the islet, he spoke this verse:

> 17. Now am I ready, my sword displayed,
>   To carve thy doom with flashing blade.
>   God will grant victory, victory to me.
>   Know, Hrafn, now, thy bane shall I be.

Hrafn spoke this verse in reply:

> 18. Poet, do not prophesy,
>   You cannot see the victory,
>   Do not claim it as your own,
>   Lest sword cleave flesh and smash the bone

Though wounds o'ercome me, boding ill,
My name will come to Helga still.

Hermund bore the shield for his brother Gunnlaug, and Sverting, son of Hafr-Bjǫrn, bore the shield for Hrafn. The one to be wounded would have to redeem himself from the duel by the payment of three silver marks. Hrafn had the right to strike first, as he was the one challenged. He struck into the uppermost part of Gunnlaug's shield, and his sword broke asunder under the hilts, for the blow was struck with great force. But the point of the sword flew up from the shield and struck Gunnlaug's cheek, and it gashed him more than a little.

Then their fathers, together with many other men, rushed straightaway between them. Gunnlaug then cried, "Now I claim that Hrafn is overcome, since he is without a weapon."

"But I claim that you are vanquished," said Hrafn, "since you are wounded."

Gunnlaug was beside himself with anger, and he maintained that nothing was proved. Illugi, his father, said that they should not make further trial on this occasion. Gunnlaug replied, "I wish that Hrafn and I may meet again like this on another occasion, when you, father, shall be too far off to separate us."

And with that they parted on this occasion, and the men went back to their booths.

On the following day it was established as law in the Assembly that all duels should be prohibited henceforth. And that was done on the advice of all the wisest men who were present, and there were then at the Assembly all the shrewdest men in the country. And that duel between Hrafn and Gunnlaug was the last one to be fought in Iceland. That was the third most numerous Assembly:[37] the first was after the burning of Njál, and the second was after the fight at Heath.

And one morning when the brothers Hermund and Gunnlaug went to the river Öx to wash, there went from the other side of the river many women, and Helga the Fair was with them. Then Hermund said, "Do you see your friend Helga, there on the other side of the river?"

Gunnlaug replied "I certainly see her," and he spoke this verse:

19. Helga was born to stir up strife,
    No peace to weave in Gunnlaug's life.
    In former years, I sought her heart,
    Swan-lovely lady—My dark eyes smart.

Then they crossed the river, and Helga and Gunnlaug talked together for some time. And when the men went back east across the river, Helga stood and gazed after Gunnlaug for a long time. Gunnlaug looked back across the river, and he spoke this verse:

20. Bright her eyes beneath her brow;
    Harm they bring in two lives now.

So after a course of time men rode away from the Assembly. But now Gunnlaug was at home at Gilsbank, and one morning when he awoke, all the men had risen up, and only he remained in bed. He slept in a bed closet, opening off from the raised floor. And there came into the hall twelve men, all in full armour, and this was the way that Hrafn came, the son of Onund. Gunnlaug sprang up at once and got a hold of his weapon.

Then Hrafn said, "There is no danger to you from anyone, but my mission to you is that which you shall now hear. You challenged me to a duel in the summer at the Assembly, and it seemed to you that proof was not made. Now I want to offer to you that we should both journey away from Iceland in the summer and fight a duel in Norway. Our kinsmen can't come between us there."

Gunnlaug replied, "Well spoken, luckiest of warriors! I will accept the offer eagerly. And here you can have whatever hospitality you wish, Hrafn."

Hrafn said, "That's a fair offer; but we have to ride away at once."

And with that they parted.

That seemed a very bad thing to the kinsmen of both of them, but they could do nothing about it because of the ferocity of the two of them. And so things had to happen as they were fated.

12. THORSTEIN'S DREAM IS FULFILLED

Now it is to be said of Hrafn that he fitted out his ship in the bay called Leiruvág. Two men are mentioned who traveled with Hrafn, both of them sons of his father's sister: the one was called Grím and the other was Óláf, and they were both worthy men. It seemed a great loss to all Hrafn's kinsmen when he went away, but he told them that he had challenged Gunnlaug to a duel since he had no pleasure with Helga. And he said that one of them must fall before the other. Then Hrafn put to sea when they got a fair wind, and he brought his ship into Thrándheim and stayed there for the winter without hearing anything of Gunnlaug. He remained there throughout the summer waiting for Gunnlaug, and he was yet another winter in Thrándheim, at the place called Lifanger.

Gunnlaug took ship with Hallfred Troublesome Poet in the north at Slétta, and they were very late sailing. But they set sail when they got a fair wind, and they reached the Orkneys a little before winter. Earl Sigurd, son of Hladvir, then ruled the Islands, and Gunnlaug went to him and remained there for the winter. The Earl showed him great honour.

In the spring the Earl prepared to go raiding, and Gunnlaug made ready to go with him. Throughout the summer they plundered widely in the Hebrides and Scotland and engaged in many fights. Wherever they went Gunnlaug proved himself the most valiant and bravest of men and the boldest retainer. Earl Sigurd returned early after the summer, and then Gunnlaug shipped with merchants who were sailing to Norway. Earl Sigurd and he parted in great friendship.

Gunnlaug journeyed north to Thrándheim, to Hladir, to meet Earl Eric, and he was there at the beginning of winter. The Earl received him well and invited him to stay with him, and Gunnlaug agreed. The Earl had learned earlier of the dealings between Hrafn and Gunnlaug, and he knew just how matters stood. He told Gunnlaug that he forbade them to fight there in his kingdom. Gunnlaug said he had the say in such things, and all through the winter he remained there Gunnlaug was continually aloof.

40

One day in the spring Gunnlaug went out, and Thorkell, his kinsman, was with him. They went away from the dwellings and into the open fields, and in front of them there was a circle of men. In the circle there were two fellows with weapons, and they were fencing. One called himself Hrafn, and the other said he was Gunnlaug.[38] Those standing in the circle said that Icelanders struck small blows and were slow to remember their boasts. Gunnlaug saw that much mockery accompanied the sport and that great ridicule was shown, and he went away in silence.

A short time after this Gunnlaug told the Earl that he was no longer inclined to endure the mockery and ridicule of his retainers about the dispute between him and Hrafn, and he asked the Earl to give him a guide into Lifanger. The Earl had been informed previously that Hrafn had left Lifanger and had gone eastwards to Sweden, and therefore he gave Gunnlaug permission to go and granted him two guides for the journey.

Now Gunnlaug went from Hladir with six men to Lifanger. In the evening he reached the very place which Hrafn, together with four men, had left that same morning. From there Gunnlaug went on into Veradale, and each evening he came to the very place where Hrafn had spent the previous night. Gunnlaug continued until he came to the highest house in the dales, and this was at the place called Súla. Hrafn had gone thence that morning. Gunnlaug did not break his journey, but he traveled away that night, and next morning at sunrise each party saw the other.

Hrafn had reached the place where there were two great rivers, and there were level plains between them. The place was called the Plains of Gleipnir, and a little headland went out into one of the rivers, and it was called Dinganess. Hrafn and his company took their stand on this headland, and they were five in number, including Hrafn and his kinsmen Grím and Óláf.

And when they met, Gunnlaug said, "Now is it well that we have come together."

Hrafn said that there was no blame for this. "And there is now a choice. Which way will you have it: that we should all fight or just the two of us? For there is an equal number on each side."

Gunnlaug said that it would please him very well either way. Then Hrafn's kinsmen, Grím and Óláf, said that they had no desire to stand aside when they were fighting, and so said Thorkell the Black, Gunnlaug's kinsman.

Then said Gunnlaug to the Earl's guides, "You shall stand on one side and help neither of us. And you must tell the story of our meeting."

And the men did this.

Then the fight began, and all bore themselves valiantly. Grím and Óláf both attacked Gunnlaug alone, and the outcome of their dealings was that Gunnlaug slew them both, but he himself was not wounded. Thórd, Kolbein's son, affirms this in the poem which he made about Gunnlaug:

> 21. Dyed anew in red blood's stain,
> With shining sword he clove his way
> To kill three foemen in that fray,
> Óláf and Grím before him slain.

In the meantime Hrafn and Thorkell the Black, Gunnlaug's kinsman, fought together, and Thorkell fell before Hrafn and gave up his life. So, finally, all their companions fell, and then Gunnlaug and Hrafn fought on with great blows. Each was fearless in the attack which he made on the other, and they fought incessantly and vehemently. And Gunnlaug had the sword which Ethelred had given him, and it was the best of weapons. Then Gunnlaug finally struck a great blow at Hrafn and cut his leg from under him. Nevertheless Hrafn did not fall down, but he drew back to a hewn tree and supported himself on the stump.

Then Gunnlaug said, "Now you are not fit for battle, and I will fight no longer with you, a wounded man."

Hrafn replied, "It is true that I have got the worst of it. Yet I have a mind to fight further, if I could get something to drink."

Gunnlaug answered, "If I fetch you water in my helmet, do not then deceive me."

Hrafn replied, "I will not deceive you."

"THE BETRAYAL OF GUNNLAUG"

And Gunnlaug went down to a stream and dipped in his helmet and carried it back to Hrafn. Hrafn took hold of the helmet with his left hand, but, holding his sword in his right hand, he struck Gunnlaug on the head and gave him a great wound.

Then said Gunnlaug, "You have evilly deceived me now, and you have behaved unmanfully when I trusted you."

Hrafn replied, "That is true, but the fact that I grudge you the embrace of Helga the Fair goaded me to it."

So they fought on again fiercely, and it finally came about that Gunnlaug overcame Hrafn, and there Hrafn died.

Then the Earl's guides came forward and bound up the wound in Gunnlaug's head, and he sat there meanwhile and spoke this verse:

> 22. No coward he who Hrafn hight,
> Ever foremost in the fight.
> Many a blow was struck this morn,
> Many a life from body torn,
> On Dinganess.

Then they buried the dead men, and after that they lifted Gunnlaug onto his horse and came with him all the way down to Lifanger. There he lay for three days, and he received all the sacraments from a priest. And there he died and was buried at the church.

And to everybody it seemed a great loss that Gunnlaug and Hrafn should die thus.

13. ILLUGI AVENGES HIS SON

AND in the summer, before this news was reported in Iceland, Illugi the Black had a dream whilst he was at home in Gilsbank, and it seemed that Gunnlaug came to him in his dream and was very bloody. And in the dream Gunnlaug spoke a verse to his father, and Illugi remembered the verse when he awoke and repeated it before others:

> 23. One blow I got from Hrafn's blade,
> One blow, and all my debts were paid.
> Yet, my own sword struck him where he stood,
> And Hrafn needs must wade in blood.

It also happened south at Mosfell that on that very same night Ǫnund dreamed that Hrafn came to him, all bloody, and that he spoke this verse:

24. Loud the clash of brands on shields,
    Red the sword that Gunnlaug wields:
    Ravens soared o'er Hrafn's head,
    I waded in my blood new-shed.

Now at the Assembly in the next summer after this, Illugi the Black said to Ǫnund at the Law Rock, "How do you intend to compensate[39] me for my son, since your son, Hrafn, betrayed him in a sworn truce?"

Ǫnund replied, "I don't think myself at all obliged to compensate you for him, so sorely have I myself suffered from their meeting. I don't intend to ask you for compensation on behalf of my own son."

Illugi replied, "Your kinsmen or your own family will have something to smart for."

And after that Assembly in the summer Illugi was always downcast.

It is said that in the autumn Illugi rode away from his home at Gilsbank with thirty men, and they reached Mosfell early one morning. Ǫnund and his sons found sanctuary in the church, but Illugi captured Ǫnund's two kinsmen, Bjǫrn and Thórgrím. He had Bjǫrn killed and had Thórgrím's legs cut off. Illugi rode home after that, and there was no redress for Ǫnund in this business.

Hermund, Illugi's son, grieved deeply for the death of his brother Gunnlaug, and he didn't think him sufficiently avenged, in spite of what had been done.

Now there was another man called Hrafn, and he was the son of Ǫnund's brother at Mosfell. He was a great seafarer, and he had a ship that was beached at Hrútafjord. And in the spring, Hermund, Illugi's son, rode alone from home, and he went north from Holtavǫrduheath and so on to Hrútafjord and to Bordeyri to the ship belonging to some merchants. The merchants were then about ready to sail, but Hrafn, their skipper, was on shore, and a great number of men were with him. Hermund rode up to him and thrust his spear through him, and then he rode off at once. Hrafn's companions were

45

all afraid of Hermund. There was no compensation made for that man's slaughter, and with this the dealings between Illugi the Black and Onund at Mosfell come to an end.

14. THE DEATH OF HELGA

As time went on Thorstein gave his daughter Helga in marriage to that man who was called Thorkell,[40] the son of Hallkell. He dwelt out in Hraunsdale, and Helga journeyed out to his dwelling with him. But she had little love for her husband, because she never turned her mind from Gunnlaug, even though he was dead. Yet Thorkell was a valiant man in himself, and he had much property and was a good poet. They had very many children. One of their sons was called Thorarin, and another was called Thorstein, but they had many children more.

And it was always Helga's greatest pleasure to spread out the cloak which Gunnlaug had given her and to gaze upon it for a long time.

Once it happened that a great sickness fell upon the farm of Helga and Thorkell, and many were ill for a long time. Helga became sick, but nevertheless she did not go to bed.

One Saturday evening Helga sat in the hall, and she leaned her head against her husband's knee. She had the cloak which was Gunnlaug's gift sent for, and when it came to her, she sat up and spread the cloak before her and gazed upon it for a while. Then she sank onto her husband's breast and died.

Thorkell spoke this verse:[41]

25. I held my dear wife to my breast,
    God took her life . . . . .
    . . . . . and now for me alone
    . . . . . there is no rest.

Helga was carried to the church, but Thorkell dwelt on in Hraunsdale afterwards. And Helga's death seemed a very great loss, as was to be expected.

And here our saga comes to an end.

The Saga of the Eight Confederates
BANDAMANNA SAGA
TRANSLATED BY MARGARET SCHLAUCH

INTRODUCTION

THE short saga about the lawsuit of eight confederated Icelandic leaders versus Odd Ófeig's son of Mel (called in the original the *Bandamanna saga*) is a jewel of prose narrative art. It is a simple story, if we consider the plot alone: a father (Ófeig) and son (Odd) separate under terms of latent hostility; the son makes good in another part of Iceland and develops into a rich and powerful chieftain; as a consequence of association with a violent and ambitious upstart (Óspak) he is faced with catastrophe through a crushing lawsuit brought against him by eight district leaders. But his neglected old father appears in the nick of time, and by astutely playing on the weaknesses of the men combined against his son—a little flattery here, a tactfully offered bribe there, the suggestion of a desirable marriage, a playing on the tensions and doubts within the group throughout—he splits the confederation, changes threatening defeat into ultimate victory, and establishes the firm basis for affectionate friendship with his son for the first time in their lives. What distinguishes the saga as an outstanding example of Icelandic storytelling is the easy skill with which it is delivered—the smooth concatenation of incidents, the steady building up of effects, the gratifying resolution at the end—and above all the virtuosity with which rhetorical and psychological effects are achieved in the transforming of situations from auspicious to inauspicious and back again.

The text has been frequently edited and commented upon. It involves a certain number of critical problems, some of which are important for an appreciation of its artistic merits and its relation to the social and cultural milieu from which it sprang. The essential facts may be briefly summarized.

First, as to the historicity of the main characters. It has been established by careful comparison with other sagas that most of these people were historic Icelanders, and that all of them were alive in the first half of the eleventh century. In the saga, Ófeig remarks that one of the confederates, Skeggbroddi, had served under King Harald Sigurd's son of Norway, commonly called Harald Hardrádi or "Hard-ruler."

49

This king acceded to sole rule of the country in 1046; hence we have a date soon after which we may assume the action of the story occurred. The main action can, in fact, be placed by internal evidence such as this at about A.D. 1050-1055. Events in most of the classical sagas fall somewhat earlier, before 1030, but the difference is one of only a single generation or so.

The second question concerns the central event itself. Here we are on less certain ground. Ófeig, Odd's father, who contrives the brilliant reversal of his bad fortunes, appears as little more than a genealogical entry in other texts. The quarrel of Odd and Óspak is mentioned, but no more than mentioned, in *Eyrbyggia saga* (Chapter 62) and *Grettis saga* (Chapter 14), with no hint of the solution here presented. Odd himself is the central figure of some short episodes and adventures related outside the *Saga of the Eight Confederates*. One of these is incorporated in a saga about King Harald Hardrádi, found in the historical text *Mörkinskinna* (put together in the early thirteenth century), as well as the later compilation called the *Flatey Book* (fourteenth century). Here we find Odd artfully tricking a royal customs inspector and even the King himself, after illegally trading with the Finns. The story is amusing but reads more like fiction than history. Odd also appears prominently in a short story about Heming Áslák's son, likewise featuring King Harald, which is recounted in the *Hauksbók* (fourteenth century) as well as in the *Flatey Book* already mentioned. It is altogether fictional. None of these stories gives any confirmation of the main event of our saga; still, we do gain the impression that Odd was important enough to have a number of stories told about himself, whether factual or fictional.

There is one analogue to the plot of the *Bandamanna saga* in another text, the short *Ölkofra Tháttr* (*Tale of Ölkofri*), where a stingy and boastful man named Thorhall, defendant in a suit brought by six chieftains, finds aid in breaking their ranks somewhat as Odd does. The legal action bears no close resemblance, but several sentences recall the *Bandamanna saga* in their very wording, and there is a similarly humorous, half-cynical stress on human vanities and weaknesses. No definite conclusion is possible about the relation of Ölkofri's tale to our saga. While most scholars have thought the tale later than the saga, Guðni Jónsson in his 1936 edition of the latter presents evidence that the Tháttr may have been composed earlier. If so, it may be that the short narrative was based on a real lawsuit, and later served as a literary model for the saga's more elaborate and consciously artistic treatment. On the other hand, Andreas Heusler suggested (1913) that the *Bandamanna saga*, a popular story, may have given rise to an imitation of its plot in an actual lawsuit—life following art. The suggestion was first made by Arne Magnússon.

All this is little more than speculation, and speculation is indeed all that is left to us when we survey the entire evidence available concerning Odd's lawsuit as an actual event. It may never have occurred. Whether it did or not, however, the saga man who wrote about it has made it as persuasively real as the most skillful reportage of true happenings could be.

The text has been preserved in two versions which differ considerably in length and wording and even in the placement of phrases and sentences. Few sentences are precisely the same in both. The two are preserved in manuscripts of the Royal Library, Copenhagen: the shorter (K) is contained in MS Gamle kongelige Samling 2845, quarto; the longer (AM), in Arna-Magnæan 132, folio, otherwise known as the *Mǫðru-vallabók*. Differing adverbs of place in the two show that they were written down in different parts of Iceland. There has been disagreement among specialists as to the relative age and merits of the two.

Mere length tells us nothing about originality, of course. A short story can be amplified as readily as a long one may be abbreviated, as Finnur Jónsson pointed out in his 1933 edition. Heusler regarded K as awkward, uneasy in its transitions, less developed in finesse and completeness of presentation. He was so impressed by the divergences that he thought the two redactions might possibly go back quite independently to a unified oral tradition. Of the two he thought AM probably earlier, because he found it closer to the smooth classical style at its best. He used AM alone for his edition, but he conceded that K, though written down later, might still conform closer to oral tradition. Finnur Jónsson, on the other hand, judged K to be the earlier (written about 1200), with AM based on it as a later, much modified redaction. His judgment was based on general tests of style, some foreign loan words in the vocabulary, and turns of expression which he considered definitely post-classical. He chose K for the text to be edited, as G. Cederschiöld had done before him (1873), while conceding that the writer of AM might have had more detailed information on some incidents such as Óspak's death at the end.

Both versions are found conveniently edited side by side in the volume prepared by Guðni Jónsson: *Íslenzk Fornrit*, VII (1936). In his introduction Jónsson rejects Heusler's theory as improbable (if the two texts were independently derived from oral tradition and written in the west and north respectively, how can they be as close in wording as they are?), and insists that both are related somehow to a lost *written* source, already a conscious work of art in that early form. "Both forms of the saga stem from a common written source or original narratives (*frumsögur*). K stands on the whole closer to this original narrative than [A]M, and there is no special evidence indicating that it was abbreviated or modified beyond what might be expected from the habits of saga writers. On the other hand there appears to be sufficient evidence that [A]M was expanded and that the style of the saga was modified in it" (p. xcvii). This would confirm Finnur Jónsson's conclusions.

The debate over K versus AM is more than a scholars' crux. It serves to remind us of the problem underlying all classical sagas: how much of them is fact, how much fiction? How, above all, was the authentic information carried down from the time of the events, mostly the latter part of the tenth century, to the age of composition and writing down, late twelfth century at the earliest? Whether or not Odd's lawsuit actually occurred, much that is told about him and his contemporaries appears to be accurate. We are amazed at the tenacity of tradition and the rich store of family and community lore that was preserved for the writers of the thirteenth century. No matter how much we credit them with embroidery, amplification, independent creation, and constructive ability, they still had an abundant heritage to draw on. Its preservation was conditioned by the peculiar forms of Icelandic social conventions, which combined a strong sense of kinship, favorable to the perpetuation of genealogies, with an equally strong community spirit finding expression above all at local or district meetings and at the general assembly or Thing.

The *Saga of the Eight Confederates* demonstrates how both these aspects of Icelandic social life contributed to the proliferation of sagas. The enveloping action, the conflict and later reconciliation of father and son, springs from the tensions within a family, where individuals at times clashed because of temperament, despite the claims of family solidarity. The central action, brought to a head at the annual assembly, springs on the other hand from the forms and codes of community life. The procedures of a lawsuit are accurately indicated without being laboriously described as an end in themselves. That is why the plot, whether true or fictional, has such a convincing air of reality. This quality has been much admired by literary critics. It is heightened by the occasional descriptions of personalities, by the skillful dialogue, and by extraordinary sustained speeches during the legal action. There is so much dialogue in some of the scenes, indeed, that they read like pure drama, the "he said's" and "he replied's" being quite superfluous. Short remarks, repartee and argument lead up to the longer discourses gradually.

An elaborately developed speech like Ófeig's against the eight confederates shows the importance of oratorical ability for litigants at the Thing. A gift like his must have been valuable. We may surmise that other speakers demonstrated a like ability on similar occasions. Though the text of the oration as here recorded is no doubt of late literary origin, it may well follow a general scheme made familiar in practice. The sinewy, idiomatic, unpretentiously effective style, the psychological appeals to listeners' weaknesses, the flavoring of satire and gossip, the planned repetitions and the steady building up to a climax, are traits of oratory which appeal also to modern readers. Even when indirectly reported—as they often appear in the sagas—the speeches are made to contribute much to the action of a story.

Because the rhetorical qualities are somewhat more amply evident in version AM than in K, the former has been chosen as the basis of the present translation, though it may have been modified and "improved" over an earlier text. This translation is based on the convenient second edition prepared by Andreas Heusler (Berlin, 1913). His few conjectural emendations are embodied here, but the interpretation of the text is different at certain points where more recent dictionaries offer what appear to be better meanings.

As for the style of the translation, a word of explanation may be necessary. To some it may appear that I have gone too far in the direction of modern idiom, especially if my rendering is compared with that of William Morris (also based on version AM). But the most conspicuous virtues of the saga bring it closest to our own times. The shrewd maneuverings of Ófeig need no learned commentary to be understood in the twentieth century. Hence it would be a pity to make them remote (and sometimes incomprehensible) by means of an artificially archaic English such as no one ever spoke at any time in the history of our language. Such a style might be defensible for the mythical-heroic sagas, which belong to no one age or place, but are on the order of fictional legends. It has no justification, however, when one is trying to convey narrative and dialogue so racy, so unstilted, so appropriate to a vigorous frontier community that it is— despite chronology—far closer to Abraham Lincoln's mode of diction in telling anecdotes than (let us say) to the Elizabethans' or even the Augustans' more formal writing. The *Saga of the Eight Confederates* in particular calls for a straightforward rendering in harmony with its treatment of the situations described. Titles of chapters have been added by the translator.

It is a pleasure to express here my gratitude to Dr. Henry Goddard Leach of The American-Scandinavian Foundation for his patient and benevolent interest in both this translation and the one which follows it. For assistance in matters of style and sense I am indebted to Professor Lee M. Hollander, whose meticulous reading of the manuscript has led to improvements on every page.   MARGARET SCHLAUCH

New York University

The Saga of the Eight Confederates

1. ÓFEIG OF REYKIR AND HIS SON ODD

ÓFEIG was the name of a man who lived in the west in the Midfjord district,[1] at the homestead called Reykir. He was Skidi's son, and his mother was called Gunnlaug. The mother of Gunnlaug was Jarngerd, daughter of Ófeig Jarngerd's son from the north at Skard.[2] Ófeig was a married man, and his wife was named Thorgerd, daughter of Váli, a woman of distinguished family and herself of excellent character and parts. Ófeig was extremely sagacious and resourceful in counseling. He was an outstanding person in every way, but not well off in money matters: he had large holdings in land, but less in movable property. He was generous in entertaining people, and yet he was in straitened circumstances with regard to supplies for his own household. He was a follower of Styrmir of Ásgeir's Creek,[3] who was looked upon as the greatest chieftain in the west at the time.

Ófeig and his wife had a son named Odd. He was good-looking and became accomplished at an early age, but he got no great love from his father. He was not notable as a craftsman.

Váli was the name of a young man who was brought up at Ófeig's home. He was good-looking and popular.

Odd stayed in his father's house until he was twelve years old. Ófeig treated him coldly for a long time, and loved him little. Report had it that no one in the district was more accomplished than Odd.

One time Odd came to speak with his father and asked him for an advance of money: "I want to go away from here. As things are," he said, "you don't esteem me much, and I am of no use to your household."

Ófeig answered, "I shall not give you less support than you have deserved. I'll reckon it very closely, and then you will

55

know how far that will get you." Odd said that he didn't find much support in that; and so they ended their talk.

The next day after that Odd took down a line from the wall and all the fishing tackle and twelve ells of homespun wool.[4] He journeyed out to Vatnsness without farewell to anyone and joined the company of some fisher folk; from them he received on credit the things most needful to him. And since they knew him to be of good family, and he was himself much liked, they risked making him the advance. So he bought everything on credit and went fishing with them that year. And it was said that the party Odd was with always had the best luck.

He was there three winters and three summers and by then he had paid back to each man what he owed him, and had earned himself some fine exchange goods besides. He never went to see his father, and each of them behaved as if he were not related to the other. Odd was very popular with his fellows.

In the course of time he went to the north, carrying goods to the Strands,[5] and made payment on a large boat; and with it he earned money. After that he made money so fast that he became sole owner of the boat, and for several summers he sailed back and forth between Midfjord and the Strands. He began to be very well off.

But finally this occupation became tiresome to him. He bought part ownership of an outgoing ship and made trading trips abroad for a while; and again he acquitted himself well and adroitly. Things went well with him, in regard to both goods and reputation. He kept up this occupation until he owned a trading vessel and the greater part of the cargo; he now went on trading trips and became a wealthy man and an influential one. He often had dealings with chieftains and men of high rank abroad, and was highly esteemed wherever he went. Now he became so prosperous that he had two merchantmen out on trips. It is said that no man in trade was at that time as rich as Odd. He also had more luck at sea than other men. His ships never went farther north than to Eyjafjord, nor farther west than Hrútafjord.[6]

2. ODD'S PROSPERITY. ÓSPAK SETTLES WITH HIM

It is told that on a certain summer Odd landed with his ship at Bordeyr[7] in the Hrútafjord district, and it was his intention to remain there for the winter. He was asked by some friends to settle down there. This invitation of theirs he accepted: he bought a piece of land in Midfjord called At Mel.[8] Here he built up a large homestead and lived there in a grand style. And it is said that in this he appeared no less noteworthy than in his trading trips before.

Now there was no man as eminent as Odd throughout the northern parts. He was better off than most others, ready to give help to those who needed it and were in his neighborhood, but to his father he never gave any help. He put his ship ashore in Hrútafjord. It is said that no one was ever as wealthy as Odd here in Iceland; indeed, that he owned no less than did three of the wealthiest put together. His property was large in every respect: in gold and silver, land and livestock. Váli, a kinsman of his, was with him, whether he was here at home or abroad. So Odd dwelt in his homestead in such esteem as we now tell of.

There was a man named Glúm who dwelt at Skridnesenni;[9] it lies between Bitrufjord and Kollafjord. He had a wife called Thordís; she was the daughter of Ásmund of the long gray hair, father of Grettir Ásmund's son.[10] Óspak was their son. He was a strong man and large of stature, overbearing and not easy to get along with; he was early engaged with transports between the Strands and the other northern parts of Iceland, an able man, and one of much bodily strength.

One summer he came into Midfjord and sold his goods there. And one day he got himself a horse and rode up to Mel, and there he saw Odd. They exchanged greetings and asked each other the news that was going about.

Óspak said, "This is the way it is, Odd," he said; "men speak well about your establishment; you are much praised by them, and all people think themselves well-placed when they are with you. Now it is my wish that this may happen to me also; I'd like to settle down here with you as your follower."

Odd replied, "Your reputation isn't very good, and you are not popular; you are thought to have a shifty look about you, as might be expected from one of your family."

Óspak answered, "Judge by your own experience, not from the hear-say of others! For rarely are things rated better than they are worth. I'm not asking any gift of you: I want to lodge with you, but provide for my own board, and then you may see how you like the arrangement."

Odd answered, "You and your kinsmen are strong, and hard to deal with, if anything should happen to cross you. But since you insist that I take you in, we may well risk it for one winter."

Óspak accepted with thanks and in the autumn he came to Mel with his possessions and very soon showed himself quite devoted to Odd; he attended to many things at the homestead and worked as hard as any two other men. Odd was well pleased with him.

The year wore on. When spring came, Odd invited him to move in with him, and said he thought it was better so. And Óspak also wished it. Óspak occupied himself with the farm work, and it prospered greatly; people thought it remarkable how well this man was turning out. He himself was popular besides, and so Odd's estate flourished, nor was any man's establishment considered more splendid that Odd's.

In one respect only he was thought to fall short of complete distinction: he did not have the office of *godi*.[11] At that time it was a common custom to establish a new *godord* or else to buy one, and Odd did so now. Followers gathered about him quickly, and all were eager to be attached to him. So for a time things remained quiet.

3. ÓSPAK BECOMES ODD'S MANAGER

ODD was well content with Óspak, and let him direct his estate in many ways. Óspak worked long and hard and was very useful on the farm. The winter passed, and Odd was more pleased than ever with Óspak, for he now took charge

of still more tasks. In the fall he fetched the livestock home
from the hills and it was very successfully done: not one
sheep was missing.

The winter passed and spring came. Odd announced that
he intended to go abroad in the summer, and said to his kinsman Váli that he should take charge of the estate. Váli answered, "The fact is, kinsman, that I am not accustomed to
that, and I'd rather busy myself with our possessions and
merchandise." Then Odd turned to Óspak and asked him to
take charge of the farm.

Óspak answered, "That task is too great for me, although
things do go well while you are there yourself."

Odd kept on urging him to do it, but Óspak declined even
though he was madly eager to accept. Finally he told Odd to
have it his way if he assured him of his help and support. Odd
said that he should deal with his property in such a way as to
become a man of the greatest importance and popularity; he
said he knew from experience that no one could or would
look after his property better than he. Óspak said the decision
was for him to make. With that they ended their conversation.

Odd now made ready his ship and had the wares carried to
it. News of this arrangement was spread about, and there was
much talk about it. Odd required no great preparations. Váli
went along with him, and when he was ready, men accompanied him to the ship. Óspak stayed with him somewhat
longer than the rest; they had much to talk about.

And when they had nearly reached the vessel, Odd said,
"There is one thing left that hasn't been settled."

"What is that?" asked Óspak.

"No provision has been made for my office of *godi*," said
Odd, "and I wish that you would take it over."

"That is out of the question," said Óspak; "I am not equal
to it. As it is, I have already taken on more than I might be
expected to manage or discharge well. No one is so fitted for
it as your father; he is highly skilled at law and sagacious."

Odd said he did not want to entrust the office to him: "and
it is my wish that you accept it." Óspak refused, though he
would have been only too glad to have it. Odd declared he
would resent it if he didn't take the office, and when they came

to part, Óspak did accept the *godord*. So Odd went abroad, and his trip went well, as was customary with him.

Óspak went back to the farm, and there was much talk about the whole affair. It was thought that Odd had put a great deal of power into the hands of this man.

In the summer Óspak rode to the Thing with a company of men, and he acted well and capably there; he knew how to conduct all matters that the law required of him, and he rode away from the Thing having acquitted himself with honor. He gave valiant support to his men and they did not lose out in any case, nor were they threatened with any attack. He proved himself kindly and ready with help for all his neighbors. There was no less hospitality and good living at the homestead than before; the work did not slacken, and all undertakings prospered.

The summer wore on. Óspak rode to the district meeting and consecrated it. When autumn came on he went up into the hills to fetch back the wethers and gathered them in successfully; a numerous flock came back, and not a single sheep was missing, either of his own or Odd's.

4. THE QUARREL OF ÓSPAK AND ODD; VÁLI'S DEATH

It so happened in the autumn that Óspak journeyed north to Svalastead in Víðidale.[12] Here there dwelt a woman named Svala. He was hospitably entertained there. She was a good-looking woman and young. She spoke with Óspak and asked him to look over her farm: "for I have heard that you are a fine farmer." He was pleased with the compliment, and they had much talk together. They got along well together, and they exchanged loving glances. And it came to the point that he asked her who had the say in regard to her marrying. "No relative is closer to me," she said, "among men of any importance, than Thórarin the Wise, the Godi of Langádale."

Then Óspak went to call on Thórarin, and was received by him no better than moderately well. He brought up his errand and asked consent to marry Svala.

Thórarin answered, "I can't say that I am eager to have you as kinsman by marriage. There is a lot of talk about your doings. I can very well see that one can't take a middle course with men of your sort: I shall either have to move her household and have her come over here to live, or else let you do as you please. Now I don't want to be drawn into this, and I won't say it is what I advise."

After that Óspak rode away and returned to Svalastead, and he told Svala how things were. So they made their own decision and she betrothed herself[13] to him by her own act, and she went to Mel to live with him. But they kept the farm at Svalastead, and hired others to run it. Óspak dwelt at Mel and kept a splendid house there. Yet he was thought to be a very overbearing man.

Now the winter passed, and in the spring Odd returned to Hrútafjord: again he had had success in his dealings and had made much money. He came home to Mel and looked over his property; he found that it had been well taken care of, and he was very well pleased.

Summer wore on. On a certain time Odd brought up the suggestion that it would be a good thing if he again took over his office of *godi*.

Óspak said, "Yes indeed; that is the thing I was least eager to take over and the least fitted for; and I am quite ready to yield it. Still, I believe it is the usual thing to have the transfer made at a district meeting or the Thing."

Odd answered, "That may well be."

Summer wore on to the time for the district meeting. And on that morning when Odd awoke he looked about and saw few people in the hall—he had slept long and deep; he got up quickly and noticed that people had already left the place. He thought this strange but said little about it; he got himself ready and some men with him, and so they rode to the meeting. When they reached it there were many people present, but for the most part they were ready to leave, for the session had already been consecrated.[14] Odd was taken aback; he thought these doings very strange. Men journeyed home, and several days went by thereafter.

It happened one day that Odd was sitting at table with Óspak opposite him; and when it was least expected, Odd sprang up from the table and made at Óspak with an axe uplifted in his hand. He ordered him to relinquish the *godord* at once.

Óspak answered, "You don't need to go after it so violently! You may have your *godord* whenever you want it, and I didn't know you were so anxious about receiving it back again." So he stretched out his hand and gave back the *godord* to Odd.

Things were quiet for a time, but from then on relations were strained between Odd and Óspak; Óspak showed himself to be rather ill-natured in his dealings. Men suspected that Óspak had intended to keep the *godord*, and not let Odd have it, if he had not been forced to relinquish it in such a way that he could not disregard it. That was the end of his work about the farm; Odd never asked him to do anything, and they did not speak together.

One day Óspak started making ready to leave. Odd behaved as if he were not aware of it, and they separated without so much as saying good-bye to each other. Óspak now left for Svalastead, his farm. Odd acted as if nothing had happened, and so things were quiet for a time.

It is now told that men went up into the hills in the autumn, and that Odd's gathering of sheep was very different from what it had been before. At the autumn counting he lacked forty wethers, the best of his stock. They were searched for far and wide over fell and hill, but were not found. This seemed very strange, for Odd was regarded as a luckier man with his herds than others. They put every effort into the search, looking for them both at home and in other districts, but to no avail. After a while they let it drop; but there was much talk about how it could have happened.

Odd was rather dejected that winter. His kinsman Váli asked him why he was so gloomy: "Or is it that you take the loss of the sheep so much to heart? You surely don't have very much self-respect if such a thing upsets you."

Odd answered, "It isn't the loss of the sheep that upsets me. It is that I don't know who stole them."

"ODD ORDERS ÓSPAK TO RELINQUISH THE *GODORD*."

"Are you so very sure," asked Váli, "that that's what happened? If so, whom do you suspect?"

Odd answered, "I won't conceal from you that I suspect Óspak stole them."

Váli replied, "Then your friendship has become very different from what it was when you put him in charge of all your possessions." Odd said that that had been the greatest piece of foolishness on his part, and that matters had turned out better than might have been expected.

Váli said, "Many men remarked then that it was a strange thing to do. But I could wish now that you would not be so quick to blame him: there is danger that such a charge may appear unfounded. Let us get together on this," said Váli; "you let me take charge of finding out just how things are, and I'll get to the bottom of it." And thus it was agreed.

Váli now made ready to depart with his wares; he rode out to Vatnsdale and Langádale, where he sold them. He was popular and easy to deal with. He continued on his way until he came to Svalastead, and there he was well received. Óspak was in very good spirits. Váli made ready to set out again the next morning. Óspak bore him company as he set out from the farm and made many inquiries about Odd. Váli said he was doing well. Óspak spoke highly of him and said he was a great and generous man. "But by the way, hasn't he suffered some losses this fall?" Váli said it was true that he had. "What do people think about the loss of his sheep? Because Odd has long been lucky with them up to now."

Váli answered, "There are various surmises. Some think it was the doing of men."

Óspak said, "That is quite likely; and there are but few who would be capable of such a thing."

"Quite so," said Váli.

Óspak asked, "Does Odd himself make any guesses about it?"

Váli replied, "He says little about it; but there is quite a bit of talk by others as to how it came about."

"That's to be expected," said Óspak.

"The fact is," said Váli, "—since we have touched on the subject—that some men consider it not at all unlikely that you had a hand in it; people put the two things together, that you two parted in a huff, and the sheep disappeared not long afterwards."

Óspak answered, "I didn't expect that you would be the one to say such a thing! And if we weren't such good friends, I'd take bloody revenge for it."

Váli replied, "You don't have to deny it nor to fly into such a passion about it. You won't be able to ward off this suspicion; I've looked over your farm, and I see that you have much more stock than would be likely if you had come by it honestly."

Óspak answered, "That isn't true! And I'm sure I don't know what my enemies are saying when my friends say such things!"

Váli answered, "What I said wasn't spoken out of enmity to you, since you are the only one to hear it. Now if you will do as I tell you, and own up to it to me, you'll get off lightly, for I shall so contrive it: I have sold my wares far and wide in the district, and I'll say that you have come by some money and bought slaughter-cattle and other stock: and then no one will suspect you. I'll manage it in such a way that no dishonor will befall you if you follow my advice." Óspak said he would not admit to it. "Then it will turn out badly," said Váli, "and you will be to blame."

Then they parted and Váli went home. Odd asked him whether he had found out anything about the disappearance of his sheep. Váli would not say much about it.

Odd said, "Now you don't need to deny that Óspak stole them, though you'd like to whitewash him if you could."

Things were quiet during the winter. But when spring came and the time arrived for the Thing, Odd journeyed with twenty men until he came to within some little distance of the farm at Svalastead.

Then Váli said to Odd, "Do you let your horses graze here, and I'll ride up to the house and see Óspak and find out if he wishes to pay for a settlement, so that a suit need not be filed."

They arranged it so, and Váli rode up to the house. There was no one outside. The door stood open. Váli went in. It

65

was dark inside, and when he least expected it, a man jumped out from the dais and struck him between his shoulders so that he fell down.

Váli cried out, "Save yourself, you poor wretch! For Odd isn't far away from the farm and he's about to kill you. Send your wife out to meet him, and let her tell him that we have made a settlement, and that you confessed, and that I've gone down the valley on a matter of business."

Then Óspak said, "This is the worst thing I could have done. I had intended it for Odd, not for you."

Svala now went out to meet Odd and said that the two of them had reached an agreement, "and Váli told you to turn back home." Odd believed this and rode home again. Váli died, and his body was carried to Mel.

Odd was mortified by what had happened. It made him cut a sorry figure, and it was thought that he came off badly in the affair.

At this time Óspak disappeared, and no one knew what became of him.

5. ODD'S CASE AGAINST ÓSPAK BROUGHT BEFORE THE THING

Now it is to be told that Odd made ready to bring this case to the Thing, and he summoned nine neighbors as jury. Then it happened that one man of them died, and Odd called another in his place. The men rode to the Thing, and all was peaceful until the time for judgments. And when the court convened, Odd advanced the charge of manslaughter, and it was duly accepted and the defense was called.

Not far away from where the court sat, two chieftains named Styrmir and Thórarin were sitting with their followers. Then Styrmir said to Thórarin, "The defense has been called in the case of the killing; do you perhaps want to undertake any defense in it?"

Thórarin answered, "I won't have anything to do with it, for it seems to me that Odd has sufficient grounds to take up the charges for the loss of such a man as Váli was, and against a defendant who is, according to my guess, a scoundrel."

"Yes truly," said Styrmir, "he is surely not a good man; and yet you have a certain obligation towards him."[15]

"I don't care if I have," said Thórarin.

Styrmir said, "You have to consider that you may have trouble—much more of it, and harder to handle—if he is declared an outlaw. It seems to me to call for consideration, and we should see what can be done about it, since we both detect a point for the defense side of the case."

"I saw that long since," said Thórarin, "yet it does not appear advisable to me to obstruct the case."

Styrmir said, "It is your affair more than anyone else's! And people rightly say that it means a disgrace to you if the case proceeds successfully, when there is a clear case for the defense. And, to tell the truth, it would be a good thing for Odd to know that quite a number of people are of some importance besides him alone: he tramples us all underfoot— and our followers too, so that no one else gets any attention. It wouldn't hurt if he learned how skilled at law he really is!"

Thórarin answered, "Let it be as you say, and I'll stand by you. But it's not anything we can expect good of, and it will surely have a bad end."

"That I don't believe," said Styrmir. He sprang up and went to the court and asked them what case was up before them. They told him.

Styrmir then said, "It so happens, Odd, that there is a mistake in the conduct of the case you are bringing up, and you have presented it wrongly: you have summoned ten neighbors as your jury from your home district, and that's contrary to law. You should have done that at the Thing and not in your own district. Now you must choose, either take yourself off from the court at once, or have us contest the suit because of the mistake."

Odd remained silent and thought over the case; he found that Styrmir was right; he left the court and went to his booth with his followers. And as he came into a passage between the booths a man approached him, someone rather advanced in years. He was wearing a black-sleeved cloak with tears in it; only one sleeve was on it, and that hung down the back. He carried a staff in his hand with a sharp tip to it. He had a wide hood on, and his eyes peered out from under it; he brought his cane down hard and walked rather stooped over. It was goodman Ófeig, Odd's father.

Then Ófeig spoke: "You're leaving the court mighty early," he said, "and it must be more than one thing you have luck with, seeing that things move so promptly and speedily for you. By the way—has Óspak been declared an outlaw, then?"

"No," said Odd, "he hasn't been."

Ófeig said, "It is not good manners to make fun of an old man like me! Why hasn't he been outlawed? Wasn't he proved guilty of the charges?"

"Guilty he surely was," said Odd.

"What's the matter, then?" asked Ófeig. "I supposed that the charge would stick. Or perhaps he wasn't the killer of Váli?"

"No one denies that," answered Odd.

Ófeig replied, "Then why wasn't he found guilty?"

Odd answered, "A mistake was found in the conduct of the suit, and I had to drop it."

Ófeig asked, "How could a mistake be found in the suit of a man as wealthy as you?"

"They claim that it was wrongly prepared in the home district," said Odd.

"That can't be, if you conducted the case," said Ófeig; "but it may be that you have greater gifts for profit and trading than for conducting a case at law successfully. But I suppose that you are not telling me the truth now."

Odd answered, "I don't care whether you believe me or not."

"It may be so," said Ófeig, "but I knew at once, when you left the home district, that the case was wrongly prepared. Yet you thought you were smart enough to do it by yourself, and you didn't care to ask advice of anyone; now you'll have to depend on yourself for this case too. You will no doubt succeed, but it is a tight corner for such a one as you, who look down on everyone else."

Odd replied, "But it's still more obvious that there's no help to be expected from you."

Ófeig said, "The only help that you will get for your suit will be if you'll make use of my advice. By the way, how sparing of money would you be if someone were to set the case to rights?"

Odd answered, "I would not be at all sparing with my money if someone would take the case over."

Ófeig said, "Then do you put a well-lined purse into this goodman's hands, for many men's eyes go squinting after money."

Odd gave him a heavy purse.

Then Ófeig asked, "Was the mistake brought up at court or not?"

"We left the court before that," said Odd.

Ófeig replied, "Then the one useful thing you did was done unwittingly!" With that they separated, and Odd went back to his booth.

6. ÓFEIG TAKES CHARGE OF ODD'S CASE

Now it is to be told that goodman Ófeig went up on the assembly grounds to the court. He came to the court for the northern district and he asked what cases were up before it. They told him that some were settled already and some were being made ready for summing up.

"How is it going with the case of my son Odd? Has it been settled?"

"As far as it can be!" they said.

Ófeig said, "Has Óspak been declared an outlaw, then?"

"No," they said, "not that."

"What's the reason?" asked Ófeig.

"A mistake was found in the suit," they replied, "and it was wrongly prepared."

"Indeed!" Ófeig remarked, "Would you permit me to go before the court?" They agreed to that. He went into the court circle and sat down.

Ófeig spoke up: "Has the case of my son Odd been judged?"

"It has been, as far as it can be," they replied.

"How so?" asked Ófeig. "Was a baseless charge brought against Óspak? Didn't he kill Váli without cause? Was the difficulty the fact that the case wasn't entirely clear?"

They said, "A flaw was found in the suit, and so it was dropped."

"What was that flaw?" asked Ófeig. They told it to him. "Quite so!" he said. "Does it then appear right and proper to you to put weight on a thing like that, of no importance whatsoever, rather than to declare the worst of men an outlaw—that is, a thief and a killer? Isn't it a great responsibility to acquit someone who deserves death, and thus to give judgment against what is right?"

They said that it seemed contrary to justice to them, yet their course was prescribed by law.

"So it may be," said Ófeig. "Were you under oath?"

"Yes, certainly!" they said.

"I supposed so," he answered. "And what was the wording of it? Didn't it say that you were bound to give such judgment as you knew to be truest and rightest[16] and most in accord with the law? That would be the way you must have taken it!" They said it was so.

Then said Ófeig, "But what is truer or righter[16] than to declare the worst of men guilty and proscribed and excluded from all sanctuary—the kind of man who is clearly guilty of theft and the killing of an innocent man, to wit Váli? But we may admit that there was an infraction of the third point the oath touches upon: that is, giving judgment in accordance with the law. Now stop to consider: which is of greater moment, the two clauses referring to what is true and just, or that one alone which applies to following the law? Surely it must appear to you—as is indeed the case, for you will surely see it so—that it is a greater responsibility for you to acquit someone who is deserving of death, when you have sworn an oath beforehand to give such judgment as you know to be most rightful. Now you must consider that this will surely weigh heavily on you, nor will you be likely to avoid having to answer for it."

From time to time Ófeig let the purse be seen peeping out from underneath his coat, and at other times he jerked it up again. He noticed that they kept casting their eyes at the purse. Then he spoke to them: "You would be better advised to give true and right judgment, as you have sworn to do, and get thanks for it and recognition from wise and upright men."

Then he took the purse and shook out the silver and counted it out before them. "Now I'll give you a proof of my friendship towards you," he said, "and how I am thinking more of you than of myself; and I do so because some of you are my friends and some my kinsmen, but each of you has great need to look out for his own interests. I will give every man of you who sits in judgment one-eighth of a mark[17] in silver, but a half mark to the one who sums up the case. And thus you will have not only received the money and discharged yourselves of your responsibility, but you will in no way have violated your oath, which is of course the most important of all."

They thought over the matter, and it appeared to them that his remarks were convincing; moreover, they thought they had put themselves into a bad position because of breach of their oath, so they chose to accept the offer that Ófeig made them. Then they sent for Odd at once, and he appeared before them, but the chieftains had by then gone to their booths. Thereupon the case was quickly taken up again, and Óspak was declared an outlaw and witnesses were named to certify that the verdict had been given. Thereafter men went at once to their booths.

No news of this got about that night. But in the morning Odd stood up before the mount of the law and announced loudly, "A man called Óspak was declared an outlaw here last night, in the northern district court, for the slaying of Váli. This is the description of the convicted man: he is large and bold-looking; he has brown hair and large cheek-bones and also black eyebrows. He has big hands, stout legs, and is of unusually large stature. His whole appearance is that of a ruffian."

At this, people were very much astonished. Many had not heard of the verdict before. It was thought that Odd had taken vigorous and successful action, considering how the case had stood.

7. COUNTER-CHARGES BY STYRMIR
AND THÓRARIN

IT IS now told that Styrmir and Thórarin talked together. Styrmir said, "We have gotten much shame and disgrace from this case!"

Thórarin said it had fallen out as was to be expected: "and clever men seem to have had their hands in on it."

"That's true," said Styrmir. "Do you see anything that can be done about it?"

"I don't know that anything can be done quickly," said Thórarin.

"What would be best, then?" asked Styrmir.

Thórarin answered, "One might make the charge against them that money was brought to bear on the judgment, and that would stick!"

"That's right," said Styrmir. They then returned to their booths.

Now they gathered together their friends and relatives for a conference. One of these was Hermund Illugi's son,[18] another Gellir Thorkel's son, the third Egil Skúli's son, the fourth Jarnskeggi Einar's son, the fifth Skeggbroddi Bjarni's son, and the sixth Thorgeir Halldóra's son, besides Styrmir and Thórarin. These eight men now talked things over. Styrmir and Thórarin told about the state of the case, and what point it had reached, and what profit they might get from Odd's property; that they might all become very well off through it.

They now reached a firm agreement among themselves to support one another in the suit so that the outcome would be either exile or self-judgment[19] awarded to them. So they entered into bond and oath on it, and now they were convinced that the bond could not be shaken, nor that anyone would be bold or adroit enough to rise in opposition. With this agreement they separated; and men rode home from the Thing, and at first all this was kept quiet.

Odd was well content with his journey to the Thing, and the relationship between father and son was closer than it had been before. For that year things remained peaceful. And in the spring they met at the baths and Ófeig asked for news. Odd said he had heard of nothing, and asked for news himself. Ófeig told him that Styrmir and Thórarin had collected a company and were planning to ride to Mel for a summons. Odd inquired whom they might want to prosecute. Ófeig told him all about their plans.

Odd answered, "That doesn't seem very serious to me."

Ófeig said, "Quite possibly it will not be beyond your powers."

The time now came for the summons, and Styrmir and Thórarin arrived at Mel with a large company of men. Odd also had many men on hand. The two brought forward their suit and summoned Odd to the Althing on the charge that he had bribed the judges, an act contrary to law. Nothing else happened there, and they rode away with their company.

It happened once again that father and son met and talked together. Ófeig asked whether he still thought the matter was of no account. Odd answered, "The case doesn't seem serious to me."

"I don't agree," said Ófeig; "do you know precisely what point it has reached?" Odd indicated that he knew what had occurred. Ófeig answered: "It's going to have more serious results than you suppose, according to my way of thinking, since six other chieftains, among the most powerful ones, have joined in the suit with them."

Odd answered, "They seem to require a considerable amount of help."

Ófeig said, "What do you advise, then?"

Odd answered, "What else but to ride to the Thing and bid for support?"

Ófeig replied: "That seems hopeless with things as they are now, and it doesn't appear to be a good thing to let one's honor depend on having the larger band of followers."

"What then is to be done?" asked Odd.

Ófeig spoke, "It is my advice that you get ready your ship by the time of the Thing session and be prepared to sail with all your movable goods before men ride away from the Thing.

73

And now, which money do you think is better placed: that which they take away from you, or that which I hold?"

"It seems to me the lesser of the two evils if you have it." So then Odd handed over to his father a heavy purse, full of silver, and so they parted.

Odd now made ready his ship and took on men for it. Time passed on to the Thing meeting. And these preparations were made quietly, so that few were aware of them.

8. ÓFEIG HAS A TALK WITH THE CONFEDERATE EGIL

Now the chieftains rode to the Thing and a great company of men with them. Goodman Ófeig was in Styrmir's party. These sworn confederates agreed on a meeting place on Bláskógi Heath: Egil and Styrmir and Hermund and Thórarin; then all rode south to the plains of the Thing. These came from the east: Skeggbroddi and Thorgeir Halldóra's son from Laugardale, while Jarnskegg came from the north; and they met by Reydarmúli.[20] Then all companies rode down into the plain and so to the Thing.

Most of the talk was about how Odd's case stood. It seemed certain to all that no one would undertake the defense; they supposed that few would dare, nor would it be of any avail, with such chieftains on the opposing side. And they themselves thought the prospects for their case very good, and boasted much about it. There was no one to say a word against them. Odd had not asked any man to help him in his case; he made ready his ship in Hrútafjord as soon as men had journeyed to the Thing.

On a certain day, goodman Ófeig went out from his booth and he was much troubled: he saw no one at all to help him and he thought his position a difficult one; he knew he would hardly be able to deal alone with such chiefs, and there were no flaws in the case they presented. He walked bent-kneed, wandering around between the booths with stumbling steps. He went this way for some time; finally he came to the booth of Egil Skúli's son. Some men were there who had come to talk with Egil. Ófeig turned aside by the booth door and waited there until the men had gone away. Egil followed them out. But when he was about to go in again, Ófeig approached him and greeted him. Egil glanced at him and asked who he was.

"Ófeig is my name," he said.

Egil asked, "Are you Odd's father?" He said he was. "Then you will be wanting to speak about his case. But there is no use in talking to me: it has gone too far for me to do anything about it. Besides, there are others more concerned in the case than I, namely Styrmir and Thórarin; these two regard it as mainly their affair, though we do follow their lead."

Ófeig answered, and a little verse occurred to him:

1. [21]More honor of yore lay
   in thought for a son;
   I never gave aught
   to the aid of Odd;
   lightly he looked on
   the law—the goose!—
   though riches he'd found
   in fullness enough.

And again he spoke:

2. [21]To a stay-at-home oldster
   it's a gladsome sport
   rather to chat with
   a knowledgeable chap;
   you'll not deny me
   your discourse, I pray,
   since men of weight
   do call you wise.

"I'll have to find myself something else to talk about by way of diversion than Odd's case; it was formerly in a better state than it is now. You'll not refuse to talk to me. It's the greatest pleasure for an old fellow to talk with men like you and so pass the time away."

Egil answered, "I shan't refuse to have a talk with you."

The two of them now went in together and sat down. Then

Ófeig began, "Do you run a farm, Egil?" He said that he did. "And do you live out there at Borg?"[22]

"That is true," said Egil.

Ófeig remarked, "Good things and agreeable have been reported to me about you: I have been told that you are not sparing of food with anyone, and you run a very fine place, and that we two are not unlike in situation: each of us is a man of outstanding family and generous with what he has, but feeling the pinch in money matters. And I have been told that you are very ready to give help to a friend."

Egil answered, "It would please me much if my reputation were as good as yours, for I know that you are wise and of a distinguished family."

Ófeig said, "Nevertheless our lots are unlike! For you are a great chieftain and have nothing to fear, no matter what comes up, and you never yield to anybody, no matter who it is you are dealing with, whereas I'm a man of little consequence. But our natures are similar. And it's a great shame that such men should be lacking in money when they're cut on so large a scale!"

Egil answered, "It may be that things may change quickly, and also for the better."

"How may that come about?" asked Ófeig.

"I'm thinking," said Egil, "that if Odd's money comes into our hands, then we won't lack for funds, for we have heard much about his wealth."

Ófeig answered, "It isn't claiming too much, to say that he is said to be the richest man in Iceland. Yet you must be rather eager to know what your share of it will be, since you stand in great need of it."

"That is true," said Egil; "and you are a good fellow and a shrewd one, and you probably have exact knowledge about Odd's wealth."

Ófeig answered, "I dare say that it's not known to anyone else better than to me; and I can tell you this much: no one has reported it to be as great as it really is. And yet I have been thinking over to myself how much you may get out of it." And a verse came to his lips:

3. Gold-lust assaults now—
   and lack-justice—truly you
   eight men of worship,[23] and
   worthless all words are.
   Gladly would I grant you—
   shield-play's-gods[24]—the
   loss of Idi's laughter[25] and
   of your honors loss eke.

"That is entirely unlikely," said Egil. "But you are a good skald!"

Ófeig said, "I'll not conceal from you how great the riches are that you'll get possession of: it is just the sixteenth part of the Mel lands."

"What! I never heard of such a thing!" cried Egil. "Then the fortune is not as large as I thought. But how can that be?"

Ófeig answered, "No, that isn't it exactly. The amount is very large. But I expect that it's the nearest to what you'll get. Did you not agree that you would get half of his wealth, and the men of the district the other half? I reckon it thus: if you are eight confederates, you will receive half of Mel farm. For in all likelihood that is what you intend to get and have agreed on; though you entered upon the arrangement in the most unheard-of manner, still, that must have been what you settled upon. Or did you perhaps expect that my son Odd would sit quiet when you make your attack on him up in the north? No indeed!" said Ófeig, "Odd will never be at a loss in dealing with you. And great as is the abundance of his wealth, he is no less rich in shrewdness and devices when he has need of them. And I suspect that his vessel will sail the Icelandic waters under him none the less, even if you do declare him an outlaw. Indeed, it isn't really a case of guilt at all when someone has been so unjustly prosecuted, and there may well come a day of reckoning for those who have been concerned in it. And I shouldn't be surprised if he is now at sea with all his possessions except only the land at Mel, which is what he intends you to have. He has heard that the sea passage to Borg is not a long one if he should wish to come to Borgarfjord.[26] And so this affair will be ended as it was begun, and you all will get shame and humiliation from it—and that will be just what you deserve—together with reproaches from everybody."

Then said Egil, "That's as clear as day; and that puts the case in quite a different light! It was not to be expected, indeed, that Odd would sit there helpless, and I shouldn't blame him for that: for there are some concerned in the case to whom I would not begrudge some humiliation from it, and they are the ones most eager to get this suit started: I mean such men as Styrmir and Thórarin, and Hermund."

Ófeig said, "It will be all the better, and no more than they deserve, if they are blamed by many people for these doings. But I should be sorry if you should come off badly, Egil, for I like you the best of all you confederates." And now he let a heavy money-purse be seen dangling beneath his cloak. Egil cast his eyes at it. Ófeig noticed that, and he quickly pulled it up again under the cape and spoke: "The fact is, Egil," he said "I think things will turn out very nearly as I have told you. Now I'd like to show you some mark of my esteem." He then undid the purse and poured out the silver into Egil's coat-lap. It amounted to 200 silver ounces of the best quality. "This you shall receive from me, if you don't oppose us in the suit; and that is, I should say, something of a mark of esteem!"

Egil answered, "It seems to me that you are a first-class rascal! You certainly don't expect that I'll want to break my oath?"

Ófeig said, "None of you are what you'd like to be; you want to be called chieftains, yet you don't know where to turn when you get into some kind of difficulty! You don't need to go about it that way; instead I'll hit on a plan by which you can still keep your oath."

"What is that?" asked Egil.

Ófeig said, "Didn't all of you declare that you would get either a sentence of exile for Odd, or else self-judgment?" Egil said it was so. "It may very well happen," said Ófeig, "that we kinsmen of Odd will be granted the right to choose which of the two it shall be. Now it might come about that the decision will fall to you: and if so I would want you to moderate it."

78

Egil replied, "You are right, and you are both a sly fellow and a clever one. Nevertheless, I shall not follow that course; neither do I have the strength nor the resources to stand up alone against all these chiefs, for their enmity would fall on anyone who rose up against them."

Ófeig said, "How would it be if someone else associated himself with you in the matter?"

"That would make it better," said Egil.

Ófeig asked, "Which one of the confederates would you prefer? Let us assume that I had the choice of all of them."

"There are two possibilities," said Egil. "Hermund is closest to me, but we don't get on well together; the other one is Gellir, and I'd choose him."

"It will cost a real effort," said Ófeig, "for I wish each of them bad luck in this, except you. But Gellir surely has wit enough to see which is the better choice: to have money and esteem, or to lose the money and get disgrace instead. But now, will you proceed in the case, if it should come before you, in such a way as to reduce the sentence?"

"That I certainly will," said Egil.

"Then let it be so agreed between us," said Ófeig, "for I shall be back to see you in a little while."

9. ÓFEIG HAS A TALK WITH GELLIR

WITH that Ófeig left and the two of them separated. Ófeig wandered among the booths, still dragging at his heels; but he was not so downcast of mood as he was infirm of gait, and not so doddering in his wits as he was staggering in his walk.[27] Finally he reached the booth of Gellir Thorkel's son and had him called out. He came out and greeted Ófeig first— for he was unpretentious in his manner—and asked what his errand was.

Ófeig answered, "I just happened to walk by."

Gellir said, "You'll be wanting to talk about Odd's case, I suppose."

Ófeig answered, "I don't want to talk about that, and I declare I have nothing to do with it; I'll find some other kind of entertainment."

Gellir replied, "What do you want to talk about, then?"

Ófeig said, "I have been told that you are a wise man, and I find pleasure in talking to wise men."

They sat down and began to converse. Then Ófeig asked, "Who of the young men out in the west, where you live, seem to you most likely to become outstanding chieftains?" Gellir said that there was a goodly choice of them, and mentioned by name Snorri the *godi* and the men of Eyr. "So I have been told," said Ófeig; "I'm sure I've come to the right one for information, since I am talking to a man who is both trustworthy and right-minded. But what women out there in the west are the best matches?" He mentioned the daughters of Snorri the *godi* and those of Steinthór of Eyr. "Yes, I have been told so," said Ófeig; "but isn't it true? don't you have some daughters yourself?" Gellir answered that he surely did have. "Why don't you mention them?" asked Ófeig. "For certainly none could be fairer than your daughters, if one may judge by likelihood. They are not married, are they?"

"No, they are not," Gellir said.

"What could be the reason for that?" asked Ófeig.

Gellir said, "Because no one has as yet presented himself who is both rich in goods and has a sufficient estate, and is also of good family and himself an accomplished man. It's true I'm not rich; still, I'm not easily satisfied in my choice because of my good family and high position. And now may I not put a question to you? What young men are there up north who are likely to become outstanding chieftains?"

Ófeig answered, "There is quite a choice of them. I shall mention Einar Jarnskegg's son first, and also Hall Styrmir's son. And some men declare that my son Odd is a very promising fellow. And now let me deliver the message that he asked me to: he would like to marry into your family and receive as wife your daughter Ragneid."

"Well," said Gellir then, "there was a time when that offer might have received a favorable reply, but as things are now I think it must be put off."

"Why should that be?" asked Ófeig.

Gellir said, "Your son Odd's case appears to be under a cloud just now."

Ófeig answered, "I'll tell you truthfully that you will never make a better match for her than this one. For it must be generally admitted that he is as well-bred a man as anyone, nor is he lacking in property and good family ties. But you are much in need of money, and it might well turn out that you would strengthen your position through him, for the man is big-hearted towards his friends."

Gellir said, "It might be considered, if this lawsuit were not pending."

Ófeig answered, "Don't mention that childish business; it shows only the folly of those who have to do with it, and will lead to their shame."

Gellir answered, "Nevertheless it is likely that it will turn out quite otherwise, and so I will not accept your proposal. However, if the case could be quashed I should be very glad to."

Ófeig replied, "It may be, Gellir, that all of you will get a fortune through this. But I can tell you how much your share will be, because I know exactly; and the very best deal possible is that the eight of you confederates all together will get half of the land at Mel. In that case your share will be small: you'll get a little money, but you will have forfeited the merit and prestige which gave you the name of one of the most important men in the country!"

Gellir asked how that might be. Ófeig answered: "I should not wonder if Odd is already at sea with all he owns except the land at Mel. You did not really expect that he would be so unresourceful as to let you decide and deal out everything he has among you? No indeed!" said Ófeig, "rather he declared if he should come into Breidafjord he might pay a visit to your homestead and he might choose any woman he wanted among your household; and that he had enough kindling wood to burn your house down if he so wished. Likewise he said that if he came into Borgarfjord, he had heard tell that it is not a long journey from the sea to Borg. He remarked too that if he came into Eyjafjord he might visit Jarnskeggi's farm. Likewise if he came into Austfjord, he might find Skeggbroddi's place. Now he doesn't care at all if he never comes back to Iceland: but all of you are likely to get out of this business only what you deserve, and that is shame and humiliation. Now it seems too bad to me that a chieftain as good as you have been should come off so badly, and I'd like to spare you that."

Gellir answered, "You are probably right, and I should not mind much if some way out of this confiscation were possible; I went along in this business according to my friends' wishes, rather than that I was so set on it myself."

Ófeig said, "Now that you are less eager about the affair yourself, it must surely be apparent to you that it would be more advantageous for you to marry your daughter to my son Odd, as I said at the beginning. Look; here is the money he sent you; and he said he himself would take care of the marriage portion, since he knew about your lack of means: it amounts to 200 silver ounces, the like of which is not easily found. Just stop and think: who else is going to make you an offer to marry your daughter to such a man, and himself to take care of the marriage portion, under such conditions that you are never likely to be insulted again, and your daughter marries into great wealth?"

Gellir replied, "This is so great an offer that I can't value it highly enough. However, nothing can make me go back on those who count on me. But I do see that I shall get nothing from the business except ignominy and humiliation."

Then answered Ófeig: "Aren't you chieftains slow-witted! Who ever urged you to betray those who counted on you, or to break your oath? It might well happen that the pronouncing of sentence may fall to you, and that you might reduce the penalty and still be true to your oath."

Gellir said, "That's quite true, and you are a foxy fellow and a sly one! But I can't go alone against all of them."

Ófeig said, "How would it be if I got another to go in with you? Would you help the case then?"

"That I will," said Gellir, "if you can bring it about that I pronounce sentence."

Ófeig asked: "What man would you want to have with you?"

Gellir answered, "I'll choose Egil; he is closest to me."

Ófeig replied, "What's that? choose the one that is the

worst of your band! It would be a hard thing for me to give him this honor—and I don't know whether I would care to do it."

"Then you decide," said Gellir.

Ófeig said, "Will you take over the affair, then, if I do get him to go along with you? For he'll surely be able to see whether it is better to get out of this affair honorably, or not."

"Since I stand to gain so much by it," said Gellir, "I think that I might risk it."

Then said Ófeig, "I talked of the matter to Egil before, and he doesn't think it so extremely difficult to handle; he has already come in on it. Now I'll advise you on how to proceed. You confederates are all of you often together in groups. No one would see anything suspicious in it if you and Egil were to talk with one another as much as you please, as you go to evening service."

Gellir accepted the money, and so it was agreed between them. Then Ófeig returned to Egil's booth, walking neither slowly nor zigzag nor bent over. He now told Egil how matters had gone. He was well pleased. Afterwards in the evening men went to vespers, and Egil and Gellir spoke together and came to an understanding between them. No one had any suspicion of it.

10. GELLIR AND EGIL PRONOUNCE SENTENCE

Now it is told that on the next day men went to the Law Mount, and great numbers were present. Egil and Gellir gathered together their friends. Ófeig also joined with Styrmir and Thórarin. And when people had come to the Law Mount, those who were expected there, Ófeig asked for silence and spoke: "I have kept aloof from the case of my son Odd up to now; and yet I know that those men are here present who have pushed it hardest. First of all I wish to call on Hermund about the case, though it has been started in an unprecedented manner, like none before it, and so conducted likewise, and will probably end in the same way. Now

I want to ask whether a peaceful settlement may be made of the case."

Hermund answered, "We won't accept anything but self-judgment."

Ófeig said, "The like of this has hardly been known of before, that one man should give self-judgment to eight others in a single suit, but there have been precedents where one man granted it to another. Nevertheless, though this case has been conducted in an unprecedented manner, I will offer to let two of your party judge it."

Hermund answered, "That we'll surely agree to, and we don't care which two they are."

"Then you must be willing to grant me the privilege," said Ófeig, "of choosing the two I want from your band."

"Very well!" said Hermund.

Then said Thórarin, "Be sure you agree only to such proposals today as you won't regret tomorrow."

"I won't take it back now," said Hermund.

Thereupon Ófeig went looking for sureties, and they were easily found since the investment was considered secure. So they shook hands on it and gave surety for whatever fine would be awarded by those whom Ófeig chose to decide upon it; but for their part the confederates pledged the dropping of the case. Now the plan was that the confederates should go up on the Thing plain with their followers. The followers of Gellir and Egil both kept together. They all sat down in one place in a circle.

Ófeig however walked into the circle, looked about him and lifted up the hood of his cloak; he stroked his arms and stood up with his shoulders thrown back. He blinked with his eyes and then spoke as follows: "Look at you sitting there, Styrmir! Surely people will think it strange if I don't choose you for the case that involves me; for I am one of your district men and I should be able to look to you for protection; you have received many a good gift from me and repaid all of them badly. It appears to me that you were the first one of all to act like an enemy to my son Odd in this matter and it is chiefly your doing that the case against him has been taken up: and so I will set you aside.—Look at you sitting there, Thórarin!"

said Ófeig. "Surely it isn't that you lack understanding to judge this case. Yet you have worked against Odd in this dispute, and were the very first to join Styrmir in taking up the suit; and so I will set you aside also.—Look at you sitting there, Hermund, big chieftain that you are! I suppose the case might be well handled if it did come under you. Yet no man was more keen about it since it started, and you made it clear that you wanted to make public this unseemly business. Nothing moved you to join in this suit but shamelessness and greed, for you have plenty of money yourself: and so I set you aside.—Look at you sitting there, Jarnskeggi! You don't lack ambition to give judgment in the case, and you'd be mighty pleased if you were called on to pronounce sentence. Your pride was so overweening that you had a banner carried before you at the Vadla Thing as if you were a king: but you shall not be king over this case, and I set you aside."

Then Ófeig looked about him and spoke on: "Look at you sitting there, Skeggbroddi! and isn't it true that King Harald Sigurd's son[28] said when you were with him, that he thought you most fitted of all the men out here for the part of a king?"

Broddi answered, "The King often spoke favorably to me, but it's by no means certain that he meant everything he said."

Then Ófeig said, "You may be king in other matters, but not in this case. I set you aside.—Look at you sitting there, Gellir," said Ófeig, "Nothing drew you into this case but avarice alone. There is some excuse for you, since you are hard up for money and you have a large household to run. Now I don't see any way of avoiding it—though all of you deserve ill instead; somebody will have to have the honor of conducting this case, since now only a few remain; but I don't wish to select those I have already set aside: and so I choose you, because you have never before been involved in an injustice.—Look at you sitting there, Thorgeir Halldóra's son," said Ófeig, "and it's evident that no case of any importance ever came under you, for you don't know how to give judgment and you have no more brains for it than an ox or an ass; and so I set you aside."

Then Ófeig looked about him, and a verse came from his mouth:

85

4. It's misery for men
   To meet old age;
   Their sight and their sense
   It steals from men.
   Once I had choice
   Of champions bold,—
   Now the wolf's tail alone
   Hangs on the hook.[29]

"And it has gone with me as it does with the wolves: they eat one another up until they reach the very tail, and they don't realize it before. I have had the choice among many chieftains, and now only the one remains of whom all will expect nothing but wickedness, since he is known to be a greater wrongdoer than anyone else; and he doesn't care how he gains money, so long as he gets it in the end. Yet this is to be considered in his behalf—even if he has been unscrupulous about such matters: that many another man has got himself tied up in this business who was formerly reckoned upright but has now forgotten manliness and honor to take up with greed and wrongdoing. Now no one might suppose that I'd choose the person from whom evil is to be expected, for there is no one as sly as he in your company: and yet I must come to him in the end, since all the others have been set aside."

Egil said, and he smiled as he spoke, "Now it happens again as it often has before, that an honor comes my way, but not because others want it to. Well, it's now up to us, Gellir, to stand up and go aside by ourselves and talk the case over."

And so they did; they stepped outside of the ring and sat down. Then Gellir said, "What shall we decide about this?"

Egil said, "It's my advice to impose a small money fine; I don't know what else will come of it, though I'm sure that we won't gain much friendship from this."

"Wouldn't it be quite enough if we impose as fine thirteen ounces of inferior silver?" asked Gellir, "—since our case was wrongfully taken up, and the worse they are satisfied the better I like it. But I am not eager to pronounce the sentence, for I expect that it will displease them very much."

86

"Do whichever you wish," said Egil: "declare the fine or take over the justification of it."

"I prefer," said Gellir, "to do the declaring."

Then they went and rejoined the confederates. Hermund spoke then: "Let us stand up and listen to Odd's humiliation."

Then Gellir spoke: "Delay won't make the two of us any wiser, and the result will still be the same: Egil and I are agreed on a sentence awarding a fine of thirteen ounces of silver to us confederates."

Then said Hermund: "Did I understand aright? Did you say thirteen *tens* of silver ounces?"

Egil answered, "I'm sure, Hermund, that you didn't sit on your ear, since you have been standing up! Certainly it is thirteen ounces, and of such money as only some poor wretch would take. It shall be paid in shield-fragments and broken rings and the cheapest trash—things you will find most unpleasing."

Then said Hermund, "So you have betrayed us, Egil!"

"Is that so?" said Egil. "Do you think you've been betrayed?"

"Betrayed, yes; and you have done it!"

Egil answered, "I hold it only right to betray someone that trusts no one else, not even himself, and I can find proofs of that in my case:[30] you hid away your money in such a fog that you imagined you'd never find it even if the thought occurred to you to look for it."

Hermund replied, "You are telling lies now as before, Egil! You told one last winter when you came down to visit me, on my invitation, from your own beggarly place, for Yuletide—and you were mighty glad of it, as was to be expected; but when Yule was past you became gloomy, as was to be expected also, and you thought it was a hateful thing to have to go back to the hungry fare at home; but when I found that out, I asked you to stay on—you and one of your followers—; and you accepted and were very glad to. But in the spring after Easter when you came home to Borg, you said that thirty unstabled old jades of mine had died, and they had all been used for food."[31]

Egil answered, "I don't think one could say too much about

your thriftlessness; and I dare say that either little or nothing at all was eaten of them. As for myself, everyone knows that neither I nor my people ever lack for food, even if my circumstances are often quite difficult; but conditions are such at your place that you had better say nothing about them."

"I just wish," said Hermund, "that we do not have to run into each other at the Thing another summer."

"Now I'm going to say something," said Egil, "that I thought I'd never say: a blessing on you for those words! For it has been foretold me that I'll die of old age, but it seems to me that the sooner the trolls take you off, the better!"

Then Styrmir said, "Surely he speaks truly who tells worst about you, Egil, and calls you a cheat."

"Now we're getting on splendidly," said Egil. "The more you insult me and find proof of what you say, the more I like it, and that's because I have been told that you had this game at your feast: you chose men to compare yourself with as to merit, and you selected me as your equal. Now it's a sure thing," he said, "that you have some disgraceful habits that other men do not know about, and you must know best the kind of fellow you are. But in this we are quite unlike: each of us promises help to others, and I do what I can, and spare myself nothing; but you run away as soon as the battle-axes are swung aloft. It is true, to be sure, that I am always hard up, and yet I don't skimp on food for anyone; but you are stingy with it, and a proof of that is that you have a bowl that you called Blesst Food, but no one who comes to your household ever knows what is in it, except you alone. Now for me it's fitting enough that my folks have a hard time when supplies are scarce; but it's much less fitting for a man to starve his household when he has no lack of provisions; and you may guess for yourself who does that!" Then Styrmir was silent. Now Thórarin stood up.

Then Egil said, "You keep quiet, Thórarin! Sit down and do not say a word! I might throw such things in your teeth that it would be better for you to have remained silent. I don't laugh about it, though the lads do so—because you sit with your legs pressed tight and rub your thighs together!"

Thórarin answered, "Good advice should be heeded no matter where it comes from." He sat down and said no more.

Then Thorgeir spoke: "Everyone can see that this sentence is foolish and silly—to impose thirteen silver ounces and no more in so weighty a case."

"I thought, on the contrary," said Egil, "that such a sentence would appear reasonable, as indeed it must, if you stop to think: for you must recall the district meeting at the Rang River[32] where a poor cottager left the mark of thirteen lumps on your head, and you accepted for that thirteen ewes with lamb as reparation; and I should suppose that this reminder would appeal especially to you!" Thorgeir said no more. But Skeggbroddi and Jarnskeggi did not wish to bandy words with Egil.

Then said Ófeig: "Now I will recite a verse for you, so that others may remember this Thing and the outcome of this suit, as we have seen it:

> 5. Warriors[33] most will vaunt them—
>   witness this—it soothes me—
>   my verses—giants' pact and
>   dwarves'[34]—of deeds that are less.
>   I, though poor in pennies,
>   put blinkers on the polls
>   of sagest chiefs, and sand
>   I sluiced into their eyes.

Egil answered, "Well may you boast about it, since no man has ever taken the wind out of the sails of so many chieftains!"

Thereupon they all returned to their booths.

Then said Gellir to Egil, "It is my wish that we stay together with our men." And so they did. There were many great clashes during the remainder of the Thing session, and the confederates were much put out with the conclusion of their case. The fee-money no one would have, and it was scattered about on the plain.

Then people rode home from the Thing.

11. ODD'S JOURNEY AND WEDDING

FATHER and son met now, and Odd was by that time all ready to put to sea. Then Ófeig told Odd that he had yielded the others self-judgment. Odd answered, "So you gave up the case, curses on you!"

Ófeig said, "All is not yet lost, kinsman!" Thereupon he recounted all the history of the case, and told Odd that a wife had been pledged to him. Then Odd thanked him for his help, and he found that Ófeig had followed up the business far beyond what he had thought possible. He told him that henceforth he would never lack for means.

"Now do you set out," said Ófeig, "as you had intended; your wedding is to occur at Mel in six weeks."

After that father and son parted affectionately. Odd sailed out with a favoring breeze northwards to Thorgeirsfjord.[35] There were some merchants already lying there at anchor. The breeze now died down and they lay becalmed there for several nights. Odd thought the wind was slow in rising, and so he climbed up on a high mountain and observed that outside the wind blew in another direction, so he went back to the vessel and gave orders to move on out of the fjord. The men from Norway mocked at them and said it would take them a long time to row over to Norway.

Odd answered, "Who knows but that you will be waiting for us here?"

And when they came out from the fjord, at once there was a favorable wind. They did not let down their sails until they reached the Orkneys. There Odd purchased malt and grain; he remained there for a time and made ready his ship. As soon as he was ready a wind blew from the east,[36] and they set sail. They had a favorable wind back to Thorgeirsfjord, and the merchants were still there. Odd sailed westwards along the coast and arrived at Midfjord; he had then been away for seven weeks.

Preparations were now made for the marriage-feast, and there was no lack of good and abundant provisions. Very many people arrived: Gellir and Egil and numerous other distinguished persons. The feast went along well and splendidly; people thought that they had never been better entertained at a wedding here in this country. And when the feast was over, the visitors were sped on their way with rich gifts, and the most expensive of all were those presented to Gellir. Then Gellir said to Odd, "I should suggest that Egil be well treated, for he deserves it."

"It seems to me," said Odd, "that my father has already treated him well before."

"Do you make it still better," said Gellir. Then he rode away and his people with him.

Egil rode away, and Odd accompanied him on the way; and he thanked him for his help: "And I won't be able to do so well by you as would be fitting; but I had sixty wethers and two oxen driven south to Borg yesterday: they will be waiting for you at home; and I shall never treat you any way but well, so long as the two of us are both alive." Now they parted, and Egil was mightily pleased, and pledged his friendship to him. So Egil journeyed home to Borg.

12. THE DEATHS OF HERMUND AND ÓSPAK

THAT same autumn Hermund gathered a band of men together and went out to the Hvamm Thing, intending to burn Egil in his house. And as they came out by Valfell[37] they heard a sound like the twang of a bowstring up in the mountain and immediately afterwards Hermund felt he was ill with a sharp pain under the arm. They had to turn around and go back, and the pain grew worse. When they reached Thorgaut's farmstead he had to be lifted from his horse. They sent for a priest at Sídumúli. And when he arrived, Hermund could not speak; and the priest stayed with him. At one time when the priest bent over him, his lips murmured, "Two hundred in the gully, two hundred in the gully." Then he died and his last hours were as reported here.

Odd dwelt in his homestead and ran it splendidly and he loved his wife dearly.

All this time there was no news of Óspak. A man named

Már, son of Hildir, married Svala, and took over the household at Svalastead. His brother was named Bjálfi, a half-witted man of great bodily strength.

Bergthór was the name of a man who dwelt in Bodvarshólar; he had summed up the case when Óspak was outlawed. It happened one evening at Bodvarshólar while the people were sitting by the fire that someone came and knocked at the door and asked the master of the house to come out. The master became aware that it was Óspak, and he said he would not go out. Óspak egged him on sharply to come out. But still he would not, for all that, and he forbade all the others to go out. And thus they parted. But next morning when the women went out to the stable, there were nine cows wounded to death there.

This was widely talked about. And once again, after some time had passed, it happened that a man entered Svalastead and went into the house where Már was sleeping. It was then early in the morning. The man approached the bed and struck at Már with a short sword so that it penetrated his vitals. It was Óspak who had done this. He spoke a verse:

> 6. From the sheath I drew forth
>   the sword new-sharpened:
>   in the maw of Már
>   I left its mark.
>   To Hildir's offspring
>   I hated to yield
>   the sweet embraces
>   of Svala the fair.[38]

And as he turned to the door Bjálfi leaped up and drove a carving knife into him.

Óspak went to the farm called Borgarhól[39] and there announced the killing; afterwards he left, and nothing was heard of him for a time. The slaying of Már was widely reported and it was severely condemned by all.

The next thing that happened was that the best stud horses Odd had, five altogether, were found dead, and people surmised that it was Óspak who had done this.

Then a long time passed during which nothing was heard

of Óspak. And in the autumn when men went after the wethers, they came upon a cave in a certain cliff and a dead man inside it, and beside him stood a basin full of blood as black as tar. It was Óspak. People thought that the wound Bjálfi had given him must have injured him badly, and that he had died from lack of care. And that was the end of him. We are not told that any charges were brought for either the killing of Már or of Óspak.

Odd dwelt in Mel into his old age and was considered a most distinguished person. Many of the people of the Midfjord are descended from him: Snorri Kálf's son and many another outstanding man. The friendship of father and son remained firm ever after on terms of close kinship. And herewith ends this saga.

The Saga of Droplaug's Sons

DROPLAUGARSONA SAGA

TRANSLATED BY MARGARET SCHLAUCH

INTRODUCTION

AMONG the sagas dealing with families in the eastern section
of Iceland, the short *Saga of Droplaug's Sons* has especial
interest for several reasons. Literarily it is noteworthy for
two scenes in particular. There is a dramatic account of a
fierce combat played out to the death in a solitary wintry
spot—a scene charged with vivid details and sharp sayings. A
second scene is built up with considerable suspense as the high
point of the revenge action which follows upon the first. The
fight by the snowdrift in Eyvindardale involves two namesakes: Helgi the son of the widow Droplaug, and Helgi
Ásbjorn's son, a powerful *godi* or priest-chieftain. The first
step in the feud of the two Helgis is a scandalous piece of
gossip (with a probable basis in fact) about Droplaug, the
mother of one of them, which is brought back to her sons'
ears. To avenge it, the brothers kill the talker, who is a
freedman of Helgi Ásbjorn's son. From this time on there
is mounting tension between the *godi* and the widow's sons.
Helgi Droplaug's son causes his namesake to lose several
cases at law; later, when the other Helgi wins a legal victory
over him (because of the suspicious killing of Droplaug's
second husband) he contemptuously ignores the sentence of
exile passed on him. Helgi Ásbjorn's son, egged on by friends
and smarting at the defiance, then plans the ambush which
is described with such effective detail in Chapter 10.

After this, the action subsides while we follow the flight
of Grím, Droplaug's surviving son. It mounts a second time,
to culminate in the account of his revenge on their enemy:
his quiet entry into the house, the hushed voices of Helgi
Ásbjorn's son and his wife before they fall asleep, the touch
of Grím's cold hand on Helgi, who mistakes it for his wife's,
the second falling asleep, the sudden blow, the outcry, Grím's
escape in the confusion. After this the story declines again
with the description (not without suspense) of Grím's hiding
places, his flight to Norway, and his eventual death there.

The characters are sharply delineated, considering the brief
compass of the narrative. The two brothers are contrasted
from the beginning, the contentious Helgi being counterposed

97

to the calmer (though none less courageous) Grím. We learn to know the widow Droplaug as a strong-minded person, an able manager, sensitive to slights, and—like many of the other women in the family sagas—capable of obtaining what she wants even while she appears to disavow the intention. It is not without significance that the saga uses her name in place of the heroes' patronymic usually appearing in titles. As a widow in charge of a farm she holds a commanding position socially; and she is likewise the source of motivation of the story, for the entire action is precipitated by revenge for the insult to her. The saga lets us know quite frankly that what she wants is sometimes not in the least admirable. We are permitted to observe her maneuvers to get rid of her second husband, since she seems to regret the alliance. The unspoken understanding between herself and her son Helgi enables him to carry out her wishes on the basis of the merest hint, especially since he had evinced hostility to his stepfather from the beginning. The plot against the latter is callously conceived, and a thrall's life is indifferently sacrificed to execute it. Though the narrative is recounted from the point of view of Droplaug's family, yet the darker sides of their characters are faithfully portrayed, along with the tenacity, the singleness of purpose, and the fierce stoicism which emerges triumphant during the combats with their enemies.

The chief enemy is also fairly treated. Helgi Ásbjorn's son is no weakling, though slow to take action. We can understand his hesitations and his reluctance to become embroiled in a feud with Helgi and Grím and their supporters, and we also admire the vigor of his action once he is aroused.

The story is worth reading, then, for its own sake, though admittedly not one of the best or smoothest of the shorter sagas. Especial interest attaches to the indications of date and means of transmission. The last sentence informs us that Helgi Droplaug's son was ambushed and killed the year after the Christian missionary Thangbrand came from Saxony to Iceland, hence in A.D. 998. This colophon has been regarded with some suspicion, since no other saga has one like it, and it may have been added later to win credence. Other sagas, it is true, attest the existence of the three chief male characters, and much of the genealogical material in the first chapters can also be confirmed from the *Landnámabók*, the book recording the early settlements of Iceland.

The precise manner of Helgi's death is not described anywhere outside the saga, however, and the whole narrative of Grím's revenge is not only unconfirmed but subject to doubt because incidents in it have literary analogues elsewhere. The visit to the house of Helgi Ásbjorn's son, the lurking in the darkness and the touch of the cold hand, recall one of the most effective scenes in the *Saga of Gísli the Outlaw*, and the possibility of borrowing by one saga or the other has often been discussed, usually on the assumption that the *Gísla saga* has influenced ours. Vigfusson and Powell, in their *Origines Islandicae*, II (1905), expressed the opinion that the action centering on Grím, the surviving brother, bears throughout the impress of fictional writing. Björn K. Thorólfsson argued in the Finnur Jónsson *Festskrift* (1928) that our tale of Grím's latter adventures has been affected by accounts of the more famous avenger and outlaw Gísli. Hence a duplication of some incidents, detracting from the plausibility of the story. For instance, Grím twice digs an underground passage or cave, and twice casts the soil into a flowing brook in such a way that his presence might not be detected. Andreas Heusler, in an article in *Deutsche Islandforschung* (1930), maintained that although the style of this saga indicates earlier, less advanced art than that of the *Gísla saga*, its plot must have been affected by some oral form of the other (in a preliterary stage?), and that hence discrepancies arose within the account of Grím's revenge. Whatever the relationship, there is some indication that the character and deeds of Grím may have been elaborated (if not created) by the composer who first worked up the raw materials of family chronicle into the present finished story.

Subsidiary materials may be briefly noted. They include the legendary and somewhat stereotyped anecdotes about the heroes' ancestors Ketil and Arneid (the beautiful slave-girl's revelation that she is a highborn captive; the discovery of buried treasure by the happy pair) and others about events which gave place-names to certain localities in the pioneering days (the drowned thralls cause a place to be named Thralls' Bight). The latter type of anecdote is abundantly represented in Old Irish literature as well as in Old Norse. The former type suggests influence from fairytale or romance, as does the concluding story of Grím's fight with a powerful berserk in Norway to rescue a fair maiden from him, and the sinister magic which causes mortal infection of his wound when he permits the berserk's witch-sweetheart to tend it. Such incidents are commonplaces in the romantic or "lying" sagas (*lygisǫgur*). We may set them aside, therefore, as patently unhistorical.

There remains considerable narrative which may be genuinely based on fact. Moreover, we are actually told here the person from whom the family lore was presumably derived, namely Thorvald, son of Ingjald, son of Thorvald, son of Grím the avenger in the story. That is to say, Thorvald the informant was the great-grandson of one of the main actors in the saga, and may conceivably have reported the events orally a century after they occurred, or even somewhat later. There still remains a gap of several generations before the writing down of the text in the latter twelfth century. We cannot assume that the informant Thorvald was the author of the literary monument as we have it. It is likely, though, as Björn Thorólfsson says in the essay already cited, that Thorvald established the order of events for later tradition, traced the family connections with original settlers, and introduced all major themes. He clearly had respect for truth, since he included such unflattering circumstances as the killing of Droplaug's second husband.

The manner of presentation also shows closeness to genuine family tradition. The pure joy in genealogy and the generally (if not consistently) accurate indications of local geography point to family chronicling. In addition, there are traits of style probably associated with saga technique from the earliest times: the conventional manner of introducing new characters, the objectivity of tone, the use of dialogue, the references to community opinion ("men thought . . ." or "people said . . ."). There are discrepancies and inconsistencies in matters of fact, to be sure. Some may be placed at the door of the composer who created the saga as a literary work. To him are doubtless due the sustained conversations and devices obviously introduced to build toward a dramatic climax. He shows a deliberate aiming for effect which at times leads to improbabilities. For instance, Helgi Droplaug's son receives a wound that cuts his lower lip from the jaw, so that he must hold it in place by biting on his beard—yet a few lines later he is able to talk quite freely.

In Chapter 3, people are represented as crossing over a frozen river—while hay is being loaded in the fields. There are also imitations, as we have surmised, from other sagas. Still, the general effect is good. Some of the curt awkwardness heightens the air of freshness and originality. Aside from the framing material at the beginning and end, and a few irrelevancies in the main part, there is a clear, logical plot, purposefully moving to its two climaxes and satisfactorily resolving all the main action. It is adorned by some of the typical Icelandic aphorisms, stoical understatements which at times heighten the drama with touches of grim humor.

The text of the saga is found, together with one of the versions of the *Saga of the Eight Confederates*, in the *Mǫðruvallabók*, which is No. 132, folio, of the Arna-Magnæan collection in the Royal Library, Copenhagen. All paper copies are derived from this. There is one surviving sheet of another parchment copy, showing enough to indicate that both manuscripts came from some lost copy, not either one from the other. The standard edition used for this translation is by Jakob Jakobsen in his *Austfirðinga Sǫgur* (Copenhagen, 1902-1903), done for the Samfund til Udgivelse af gammel nordisk Litteratur, XXIX, pp. 141-80. A partial translation was published, along with the complete Icelandic text, by Gudbrand Vigfusson and F. York Powell in their *Origines Islandicae*, II, pp. 528-61, but this gives only the part dealing with the fight in Eyvindardale. The present translation is, so far as I know, the only complete one in English. Chapter titles have been added by the translator.

MARGARET SCHLAUCH

New York University

The Saga of Droplaug's Sons

1. ABOUT KETIL AND ARNEID

KETIL was the name of a man who was called Din; he dwelt in Skridudale[1] at Húsastead. There was a man called Atli, Ketil's brother; he was surnamed Atli Porridge. The two men had one homestead together and were very well off; they were always traveling abroad with wares for sale and they became very rich. They were sons of Thidrandi.

One spring Ketil made ready his ship in Reydarfjord—for it was lying ashore there—and afterwards they sailed out to sea. They were out for a long time, and in the fall they landed at Konungahella[2] and there they berthed their ship. Then Ketil bought horses, and with twelve men he rode eastward to Jamtaland until he reached the place of a man named Véthorm. This man was a great chief and a good friend of the two brothers. Véthorm was the son of Rognvald who was the son of Ketil of Raumsdale. Véthorm had three brothers: one was called Grím, the second Gutthorm, and the third Ormar. All the brothers were great warriors; in the winter they lived with Véthorm, but in the summers they went out on viking expeditions.

Ketil remained here during the winter with his men. There were two women of unknown origin with Véthorm; the one of them did all the work that she was able to, but the other, who was the elder, sat and sewed. The younger did everything well, but she was badly requited, and she often wept. Ketil reflected on this.

One day after Ketil had been there a short time, this woman went out to the river with the clothes and washed them. Then she washed her hair, and it was fair and abundant and became her well. Ketil knew where she had gone, and he went to her and said to her, "What manner of woman are you?" he asked.

"My name is Arneid," she replied.

Ketil asked, "What is your family?"

She answered, "I think that does not concern you."

He pressed her closely about it, and asked her to tell him. Then she said weeping, "My father was named Ásbjorn and he was called Skerry-blesi; he ruled over the Hebrides and was Jarl there after the death of Tryggvi. Later Véthorm made raids there with all his brothers, in eighteen ships. They fell upon my father's homestead at night and burnt him in it, together with all his men. But the women were allowed to go out, and they carried off my mother Sigrid and me and brought us here, but the other women were all sold as slaves. Gutthorm is now the ruler of the islands."

Then they parted. But on the next day Ketil spoke to Véthorm and said, "Will you sell Arneid to me?"

Véthorm answered, "You shall have her for half a hundred[3] silver pieces, because of our friendship."

Then Ketil offered him money to cover her maintenance, "because I don't want her to work." But Véthorm said he would give her board as he gave it to Ketil's other companions.

This same summer Grím and Ormar, Véthorm's two brothers, came home; they had made raids in Sweden that season. Each of them had his own merchant ship, and both were laden with wares. The brothers remained with Véthorm during the winter, but in the spring they made ready their ships for Iceland, and it was the intention of Ketil and his men to sail with them. When they were lying before the Vík,[4] Arneid asked Ketil to let her go ashore and gather fruit, together with another woman. He gave her leave, but told her to go but a short distance.

They went ashore and came to the foot of a ridge, and a great rain fell on them. Arneid said, "Go to the ship and tell Ketil to come to me, for I feel ill."

She did this and Ketil went out alone to Arneid. She greeted him and said, "I have found some coals here."

Together they dug in the sand there and found a chest full of silver, and then they returned to the ship. Thereupon Ketil offered to take her to her kinsfolk with this wealth, but she chose to follow him.

After that they sailed out to sea and were separated from the others. Ketil reached Reydarfjord in his ship and drew it up on the land; and afterwards he went to his dwelling at Húsastead. Half a month later Ormar reached Reydarfjord in his ship. Ketil offered him hospitality, and his ship was drawn ashore. The same summer Grím sailed to Eyrar and into the haven called Knarrarsund,[5] and he stayed that winter with a man called Thorkel. The following spring Grím took for himself the land which was called Grímsness[6] from that time on, and he dwelt at Burfell all his life.

2. KETIL'S GRANDSON MARRIES DROPLAUG; THEIR FAMILIES

Now it is to be told that Ketil Din bought land for himself to the west of the lake which is called Lagarfljót. The farm was called Arneidarstead;[7] and here he lived from that time on. At the spring Thing, Ketil bought land for Ormar, which then was called Ormarstead; it was somewhat farther out along the lake, and here Ormar dwelt until his old age. Next, Ketil bought the office of *godi*,[8] and gave silver for it. Before that he and his brother Atli Porridge had divided their possessions between them. Atli bought land east of the Fljót and beyond Hallormstead, which place is now called Atlavík,[9] here he lived until his old age, but now there are only roofless walls of sheep-pens there.

After that Ketil held a wedding with Arneid, for she was a very excellent woman. They had a son named Thidrandi, who was a tall man and handsome. Ketil did not live long, and so Thidrandi took over his possessions and the office of *godi* after him.

Hávar was the name of a man; he was the son of Bessi who was called the Wise. Hávar dwelt at Vallaness. He had a wife and two children; Bessi was his son and Yngvild his daughter, and she was considered to be a very good match. Thidrandi asked for her in marriage, and she was given to him.

A certain man named Egil had taken all of the land around the Nordfjord for himself, and he dwelt at a place called the Ness. He was called Egil the Red, and he was Guttorm's son. He was married and had a daughter named Ingibjorg. Bessi Hávar's son asked for her, and she was given to him. Nessland went with her as dowry.

Thidrandi and Yngvild had many children. Ketil was one son, and a second was Thorvald. Jóreid was their daughter, who was married to Sídu-Hall; a second daughter was Hallkatla, married to Geitir Lýting's son who dwelt in Krossavík in Vapnafjord district; a third daughter was Gróa, who dwelt out in the district at Eyvind River[10] settlement. Her son was Bard.

When Ketil and Thorvald had grown up, their father Thidrandi fell ill and died. They inherited his property, but were not able to agree on owning it together for any time. Thorvald was a large, strong man, silent and trusty, and influential in his district. Ketil was of a cheerful disposition and outstanding in lawsuits. They divided the property and Thorvald took Arneidarstead, but Ketil became *godi*. He lived at Njardvík and he was a great chieftain.

Thorgrím was the name of a man who dwelt at Giljar, to the north in Jokulsdale. He had a wife and a daughter named Droplaug; she was a fair woman, and very clever in all things. Thorvald asked for Droplaug's hand, and they were married. They had two sons; the older was called Helgi and the younger Grím. There was one year's difference between them.

Thorvald did not live to become an old man. After his death Droplaug went on living at the place with her two sons. Helgi was very large in stature, fair and strong, cheery and boisterous. He did not wish to be concerned with the farm, but he was most skilled in arms. Grím was also a large man, very strong, but silent and self-contained; he was an excellent husbandman. The two brothers practised all sorts of athletic feats, so that they were reckoned ahead of all other young men in what they did, and their like could not be found.

3. HELGI AVENGES THE INSULT
PUT ON DROPLAUG

THERE was a man named Bessi who dwelt at Bessastead ;[11] he
was the son of Ossur. Bessi's son Holmstein lived at South
Vídi fields.[12] He was married to Áslaug Thórir's daughter,
the sister of Hrafnkel the Godi. Hallstein was the name of
a man who lived in North Vídi fields; he came from Breid-
dale, and he was both rich and well-liked. His wife was
Thorgerd. They had three sons: Thórd and Thorkel and
Eindridi.

There was a man named Thorgeir who lived in Hrafnkels-
stead. Helgi Ásbjorn's son dwelt in Oddstead up above Hafr
Creek. He was the *godi* there; his wife was Droplaug[13] the
daughter of Bessi the Wise, and they had many children.
Hrafnkel[14] was the name of a cousin of Helgi Ásbjorn's son;
he was a young man and lived at Hafr Creek. He and Helgi
Ásbjorn's son shared the office of *godi*, and Helgi was the
one who discharged it.

There was a man named Án the Juggler who dwelt at
Gunnlaugstead below Mjófaness. Ossur was the name of a
man who dwelt below the Ás ridge, west of the Fljót; he was
a kinsman by marriage of Helgi Ásbjorn's son. Hjarrandi
was the name of a man who lived at Ongul River, to the east
of it, and out in the fields; he was married to a daughter of
Helgi Ásbjorn's son who was called Thorkatla. It is said
that Ossur was a wise man and well versed in law cases.

There was a man named Bjorn who dwelt at Mýrar west
of the Geitdale River;[15] he was called Bjorn the White. He
too was married to a daughter of Helgi Ásbjorn's son.

It was the custom in those days to carry food to women
who were lying in, and so it happened that the Droplaug who
was Helgi's wife went to visit her mother Ingibjorg in Bessastead, and two thralls went along with her; they drove
two oxen and a sledge attached. Droplaug remained there
only one night, since there was to be a feast at Ormarstead the
next evening; that was a little before the time of the spring
Thing. Afterwards they went home, driving over the ice, and

when they came out by Hallormstead,[16] the two thralls rode in the sledge, for the oxen knew their way home. But when they came to the inlet south of Oddstead, the oxen plunged into a hole in the ice and they were all drowned there. The place has been called Thralls' Vík ever since. Helgi's shepherd reported the news to him alone, and Helgi instructed him to tell no one.

After that Helgi went to the Thing. There he sold Oddstead and bought Mjófaness. He moved over there, since it seemed to him that here he could forget more quickly the death of his wife Droplaug. Somewhat later he asked for Thórdís Todda, daughter of Brodd-Helgi, in marriage, and she was given to him.

There was a man named Thórir who dwelt on Mýness[17] east of the lake; he was a married man and very wise. On the farm with him there dwelt a man called Thorgrím Dung-Beetle.

Thorfinn was the name of a man who worked as hired laborer in the summer, but in the winter he was without fixed abode, and carried wares about with him for sale. One autumn he was staying at the house of Thórir of Mýness. He sat by the fire with the men servants and they were having a great discussion about which women in the district were most noteworthy. They were agreed that Droplaug of Arneidarstead surpassed most of them. Then Thorgrím said, "It might be so, if she had always contented herself with her own husband."

They answered, "We have never heard any rumors on that score." At that moment the husbandman Thórir came up and bade them stop that talk at once.

When the night had passed, Thorfinn departed. Next he came to Arneidarstead and told Droplaug all the talk among the men servants of Thórir. She gave the matter little attention at first, except that she became very silent.

One morning Helgi asked his mother what ailed her. She told her two sons how Thorgrím Dung-Beetle had slandered her; "yet you two will avenge neither this insult nor any other, though it touches me."

They acted as if they did not hear what she said. At this time Helgi was thirteen years old, and Grím was twelve. A little later they made ready to leave home, and said they intended to visit their kinswoman Gróa at the Eyvind River. They crossed over the ice of the Fljót and remained there one night, but the next morning they arose early. Gróa asked what they were going to do. They answered "We are going to hunt grouse."

They went on to Mýness and there they found one of the women. They asked her for the husbandman. She told them that he had gone out on the sandbanks with seven others.

"What are the men servants doing?" asked Helgi.

She answered "Thorgrím Dung-Beetle and Ásmund went out to get hay on the island."

Then they left the farm and followed the rocky ridge where the Jarnsída Creek flows, and so they approached the men on the island. Ásmund was on top of the hay-sled and he saw the brothers coming, and recognized them. They unhitched the horse from the sledge, for Thorgrím meant to escape by riding to the farm; but as he was about to leap on the horse, Helgi cast a spear through his middle, and Thorgrím fell down dead. Ásmund drove the hay sled home, much frightened.

The brothers now returned to the Eyvind River. Gróa asked what they had bagged on the hunt. Helgi said, "We have just killed a dung-beetle."

Said she, "Though you may think that killing a matter of no moment, Thórir is a man of importance, and you should now go home to Arneidarstead."

This they did, and they kept about them a great number of men.

4. HELGI DROPLAUG'S SON HELPS HRAFNKEL AT THE THING

IN THE evening Thórir came home and heard news of these doings. He said that this event did not concern him, since Thorgrím was the freedman of Helgi Ásbjorn's son. Then he went to Helgi and told him about the slaying: "and I consider that it is for you to take up this matter." Helgi said that was true. Then Thórir went home.

One day Droplaug said to her sons, "I will send you to Geitir at Vapnafjord in Krossavík."

They left home, going westwards over the mountains, and when they had gone a quarter of the way a great snowstorm overtook them and they did not know which way they were headed until they reached the wall of a house. They went about it in a sunwise direction. Then they found a door, and Helgi knew that that was the house in which Bessi the Wise made heathen sacrifice. They went away and returned home to Arneidarstead when most of the night had passed. But the storm lasted for half a month, and people thought that was a long time indeed. Bessi the Wise said the snowstorm had lasted so long because the sons of Droplaug had gone about his house of sacrifice in sunwise direction, and also because they had not made known the slaying of Thorgrím Dung-Beetle according to law, and that the gods were therefore angry.[18]

Bessi now went to see the brothers, and they announced the slaying openly, afterwards they went north to Geitir at Krossavík. In the spring following, Helgi and Grím and Thorkel Geitir's son went to the Thing at Kraki Creek in Fljótsdale; here they met Helgi Ásbjorn's son and made atonement for the killing of Thorgrím, and Thorkel paid for it. But Helgi Droplaug's son was resentful because money was paid for the slaying of Thorgrím, and it seemed to him that the slander was still unavenged.

The two brothers remained at Krossavík, and Helgi learned about law dealings from Thorkel. Helgi took up lawsuits, especially those against Helgi Ásbjorn's son's followers at the Thing. The two brothers constantly with their mother.

Eindridi Hallstein's son had gone abroad. He was taken in Ireland and held captive there. His brothers Thorkel and Thórd heard this, and they sailed from Iceland and ransomed him, and then they returned to Iceland. Hallstein's wife had died by this time, and so he asked for Droplaug and received her in marriage. But Helgi said it was not according to his will. Afterwards she went to live with Hallstein at Vídi fields.

The brothers Helgi and Grím journeyed out to Tunga[19] with ten others to see a husbandman who was called Ingjald, Nidgest's son. He had a daughter named Helga, whom Grím asked for in marriage, and she was given to him. Then Ingjald sold his land, and bought the half of Arneidarstead. Here Grím and his father-in-law lived together, but Helgi Droplaug's son was sometimes with them and sometimes at Krossavík.

Hrafnkel asked to share the office of *godi* with his kinsman Helgi Ásbjorn's son, but he did not obtain it. Then he went to see Holmstein at Vídi fields and asked him for aid. Holmstein said, "I myself shall not oppose Helgi Ásbjorn's son, since he is married to my sister. But it is my advice that you ask Helgi Droplaug's son to help you, and I shall get my followers to back you."

Then Hrafnkel went to see Helgi Droplaug's son and asked for his help. Helgi replied, "It seems to me Holmstein should regard his marriage to your sister as more important than matters which are past."

Hrafnkel asked Helgi to aid him. Then Helgi said, "I advise you to go out to Gunnlaugstead at the end of a week and meet Án the Juggler and praise him highly." (There was great friendship between him and Helgi Ásbjorn's son because Án had given him many rich gifts.) "You should ask Án what honors he thinks he has received from Helgi, and praise Helgi at every turn. And if he shows he is pleased at this report about Helgi, then ask him if he has ever been appointed associate of the *godi* Helgi Ásbjorn's son. If Án says he never has attained this, tell him it would be better to give Helgi Ásbjorn's son his stallion in order to obtain the honor of sitting in court."

After this they parted, and some time later Hrafnkel visited Án and spoke to him as Helgi had suggested. Án said he would try Helgi's counsel. Then Hrafnkel rode home. In the spring men journeyed to the Thing. Then Helgi Ásbjorn's son appointed Án the Juggler as associate, but the matter was to be kept secret, since Án had given Helgi Ásbjorn's son seven stud horses altogether. And when Án took his place as associate judge, Helgi put a felt hood on his head to conceal him and bade him keep his peace.

Then Hrafnkel came to the court, and the sons of Droplaug and many men with them. Helgi Droplaug's son approached the court where Án the Juggler sat. Helgi thrust the hilt of his sword under the felt hood and struck it off him and asked who it was that was sitting there. Án gave his name. Helgi said, "Who appointed you by right of his office?"

He answered, "Helgi Ásbjorn's son did it."

Then Helgi Droplaug's son called on Hrafnkel to summon witnesses and call on Helgi Ásbjorn's son to give up the office of *godi*.[20] He said that all suits were void, since he had appointed Án the Juggler as judge.

Thereupon a great crowd of men gathered, and the crowd almost came to blows when Holmstein went between them and sought to bring about an agreement. It was decided that Hrafnkel should hold the office of *godi* as long as Helgi had had it before, and after that they should both hold it together, and Helgi should give Hrafnkel aid in all cases at the Thing and at all meetings, and wherever he had need of help. Helgi Droplaug's son said to Hrafnkel, "It seems to me that I have given you great help." Hrafnkel said it was true.

And now men went home from the Thing.

5. HELGI DROPLAUG'S SON WINS A SECOND CASE

THE winter afterwards there was a great famine and loss of livestock. Thorgeir, the husbandman of Hrafnkelstead, lost very many of them.

There was a man named Thórd who dwelt at Geirolfseyr, west of Skridudale River. He was a rich man, and he was fostering the child of Helgi Ásbjorn's son. Thorgeir went to him and bought fifty ewes from him, giving wares in payment. He had little good of these ewes, for they got away from him. In the fall, Thorgeir himself went to look for them, and within the pen at Geirolfseyr he found eighteen ewes belonging to him, and they had been milked. He asked the women who had told them to do that, and they said it was Thórd. Then he went to see Thórd and bade him make good the wrong. He made easy conditions, bidding him either to give back the same number of two-year old wethers, or to feed the ewes during the winter. But Thórd refused both. He said it was little benefit for him to be fostering Helgi Ásbjorn's son's child if he had to pay indemnity for this.

Then Thorgeir went to see Helgi Ásbjorn's son and told him the story. He answered, "It is my will that Thórd pay you indemnity, and your claim is justified. Report my words to him."

Thorgeir now sought Thórd again, but he gained nothing by it. After that he went to see Helgi Droplaug's son and asked him to take up the case: "and I wish you to receive what is gained by it," he said. And on these terms Helgi took over the case.

In the spring Helgi Droplaug's son went to Geirolfseyr and summoned Thórd to the Althing; he accused him of having concealed the ewes like a thief and of stealing their milk. Later the case went before the Thing, and Helgi Droplaug's son and Thorkel Geitir's son came with a great host of men; Ketil of Njardvík was with them. Helgi Ásbjorn's son did not have followers enough to void their suit. So men asked them to come to an agreement; yet Helgi Droplaug's son would have only self-judgment, and on this basis they reached an agreement. Helgi was paid as much value in cows as the ewes had been worth which Thórd had milked. Thus the matter was settled, and Helgi Droplaug's son thought that it had gone according to his wishes.

6. HELGI DROPLAUG'S SON WINS ANOTHER CASE AGAINST HELGI ÁSBJORN'S SON

There was a man named Sveinung who lived at Bakki in the Borgarfjord district;[21] he was the son of Thórir, and was a large man, strong and wise. He was a friend of Helgi Droplaug's son. The winter following, Helgi Droplaug's son spent a long time with Sveinung at Borgarfjord.

Thorstein was the name of a man who dwelt at Desjarmoor in the Borgarfjord district; his wife was Thordís, who was closely related to Helgi Droplaug's son. A man named Bjorn dwelt at Snotruness in Borgarfjord; he was married, but he was not content with his wife alone. Thorstein was foster-father of a child of Helgi Ásbjorn's son. Bjorn was constantly going to Desjarmoor to talk with Thordís, Thorstein's wife. Thorstein had grown old at this time, and she had been given him for money, but he was none the less a well-preserved man.

One time Thorstein spoke with Helgi Droplaug's son and bade him try if Bjorn might not be persuaded by him to leave off visiting Thordís. Helgi was unwilling, but he promised to try it some time.

A certain time Bjorn went by night to Desjarmoor, but Helgi and Sveinung went to meet him. Helgi said to him, "I wish very much, Bjorn, that you leave off these visits to Thordís, for it is no honor to vex an old man. Yield to my words now, and another time I will do the like for you."

Bjorn made no answer, but continued on his way. A second time Helgi met Bjorn as he was leaving Desjarmoor, and he asked him mildly to give up his trips thither. Bjorn said, as usual, that he would not. The result of the affair was that Thordís went with child, and it was quickly known over the whole district. Helgi had taken up the case for Thorstein, and he asked Bjorn to make amends, but he replied that he would make no atonement nor be held answerable for it. Then Helgi struck Bjorn dead and proclaimed him outside the law since he was slain with just cause. The next night Helgi and Sveinung and two other men carried Bjorn out to a skerry which lay near the land and buried his body, and the place has since been called Bjorn's Skerry.

Men were sent with the news to Helgi Ásbjorn's son at Mjófaness, and it seemed to Bjorn's wife that she ought to obtain support from him for the case against the slayer. The spring after, Helgi Ásbjorn's son went to make ready the case at the Borgarfjord Thing, but he did not find Bjorn's body. Then Helgi Ásbjorn's son summoned Helgi Droplaug's son and charged him with murdering a man and sinking the body in the sea instead of burying him in the earth. Helgi brought this up as a case for outlawry before the Thing. Helgi Droplaug's son had prepared the charges of unlawful cohabitation for the Thing.

Now both cases were brought before the Althing for court judgment. Helgi Ásbjorn's son called on the other side to make its defense. Helgi Droplaug's son went before the court, and many men with him; he named witnesses to prove that all of Helgi Ásbjorn's son's charges were void, and he said three men were present who saw Bjorn buried. Sveinung and two other men swore at the altar-ring that they saw Bjorn buried. Thus all of Helgi Ásbjorn's son's charges were quashed. Helgi Droplaug's son wished to have judgment declared against Bjorn as having incurred outlawry, but Helgi Ásbjorn's son offered money indemnity in place of that, and it was left to Helgi Droplaug's son alone to decide the amount. He awarded himself one hundred ounces of the silver then current, and with that they parted.

7. DROPLAUG'S SECOND HUSBAND KILLED

SOME seasons later Helgi Droplaug's son went on the way from the autumn Thing to North Vídi fields to visit Hallstein his stepfather and his mother. He had not been there since she had been married. Droplaug told her husband that he should invite Helgi to remain there all winter. He answered, "I do not care very much to do that; I should rather give him oxen or horses." But because she urged it, he asked Helgi to stay there, and Helgi accepted.

Hallstein had a thrall named Thorgils. A fortnight later Helgi and Droplaug and the thrall Thorgils talked together for a long time one morning, and no one else knew what they said. Thorgils was busy with the sheep during the winter in a fenced field south of the yard. He was a good workman. Much hay had been carried thither.

One day Thorgils came to Hallstein and bade him come out to look at his hay and livestock. He went there and entered the shed, intending to go out by the window, but at this moment Thorgils struck at Hallstein with an axe belonging to Helgi Droplaug's son, and that was all he needed for his death.

Just then Helgi came down from his horses on the slope up above, and he saw that Hallstein was slain; at once he killed the thrall. He went home and told his mother the news as she was sitting by the fire with the women about her. A little later the report sprang up among the people of the farm at Vídi fields that Helgi and Droplaug and Thorgils had been talking a long time together one day before Hallstein was slain, and the killing caused much unfavorable comment.

Helgi Ásbjorn's son took up the case and summoned Helgi and Droplaug on a charge of plotting Hallstein's death, and he made ready the matter for the Thing. The case of Helgi Droplaug's son was regarded with disfavor; and no men would give him aid for it except Thorkel Geitir's son and Ketil Thidrandi's son. But when men had left their homes for the Althing, Droplaug took the possessions which she had shared with Hallstein and went aboard a ship in Berufjord with her three-year-old son Herjolf. They left Iceland and went to the Faroe Islands. Here she bought land and remained on it until her old age; and so she is out of the saga.

8. HELGI DROPLAUG'S SON IS EXILED BUT DEFIES THE OTHER HELGI

HELGI ÁSBJORN'S SON had taken over the case because there were no sons of Hallstein in the country. He had many followers at the Thing. Now people sought to bring about an agreement between the namesakes, with no other result than that Helgi Ásbjorn's son had the sole decision. The agreement was that 1200 pieces of silver, and to the value of five cows, was to be paid for the killing of Hallstein, and Helgi Droplaug's son was to go into exile for three winters, and he might remain but one night in his house before he departed.

If he did not go, he would fall forfeit to Helgi Ásbjorn's son between Smjórvatnsheath and Lónsheath.[22]

Helgi Droplaug's son made no effort to go abroad. Then his brother Grím left his dwelling and joined Helgi. And together they stayed that winter with Thorkel at Krossavík; they went about the whole district to gatherings of men and to assemblies just as if Helgi were not exiled. Soon after, the sons of Hallstein, Thórd and Thorkel, made land in Reydarfjord, but his son Eindridi had died before they arrived in Ireland. They gave Helgi Ásbjorn's son timber for a hall, and thus they rewarded him for taking up the case of the slaying of their father. The hall he built is still standing on Mjófaness.

Thorgrím called Fur-cap dwelt in Midby in the Nordfjord district;[23] his wife was Rannveig Bresting. She was a sister of Thordís, Thorstein's wife, and related to Helgi Droplaug's son. In the spring at the Múli Thing she asked her kinsman Helgi to come and divide the property between Thorgrím Fur-cap and herself, preparatory to a divorce, and it came about that Helgi promised the visit.

A few winters before this the two namesakes had met at the autumn Thing at Thinghofdi; at that time Helgi Droplaug's son was to pronounce the law proceedings, and he made a slip of the tongue in doing so. Men laughed much at his expense, and Helgi Ásbjorn's son smiled. Helgi Droplaug's son noticed this, and said, "Hrafnkel is standing behind you, Helgi."[24]

"That is no reproach for me," replied he; "but I want you to know that there will be a meeting between us from which both of us will not come away unharmed."

Helgi Droplaug's son answered, "I have no fear of these threats, terrible though they may be, for I expect to cover your head with rocks after that meeting."[25]

Thus they ended their talk at that time.

9. PREPARATIONS OF THE TWO HELGIS

THE next spring Flosi of Svínafell sent word to Thorkel Geitir's son telling him to collect followers for him from the north. Flosi wished to have Arnór Ornólf's son, brother of Halldór at Skógar, declared an outlaw; Flosi had had Halldór slain. Thorkel gathered a band of men, and they numbered thirty in all. He asked Helgi Droplaug's son to go with them. Helgi answered, "I should be bound to go with you, and am eager to besides, but I am ill and shall remain at home."

Thorkel asked Grím if he would go along, but Grím replied that he could not leave Helgi while he was ailing. Then Thorkel went south of Svínafell with his thirty men, and thence he and Flosi went to Skógar with a hundred[26] men.

A little later Helgi spoke with his brother Grím and told him that now he wished to set out for a visit to his kinswoman Rannveig and divide her possessions with Thorgrím Fur-cap. Thorkel and Gunnstein of Inner Krossavík and two men of their household went with them, six men in all. They journeyed eastwards across the mountains and came to Thorkel at Torfastead,[27] whose daughter was Tófa, called the Light of the Hlid. She was the sweetheart of Helgi Droplaug's son. The men remained there that night, and she and Helgi spoke much together. She had a premonition that he would never return from this journey. She went down the road with them at parting, weeping bitterly. Helgi unfastened a handsome belt he had on, with a knife in it, and gave it to her. After that they parted.

The men rode on to the homestead which was called Straum, and a man named Helgi the Thin went on with them from there; they now numbered seven in all. They reached Eyvind River at Gróa's place, and were well received there. Thorbjorn was the name of a servant of Gróa's who was very skillful with weapons. Helgi Droplaug's son asked him to sharpen his sword while he was going down to the fjords, and Thorbjorn gave Helgi another sword.

Thence they rode to the Nordfjord[28] to see Thorstein, his kinsman by marriage; he was married to Thordís the sister of Rannveig who was Thorgrím Fur-cap's wife. On the day when Helgi was staying there, Thorkel the brother of Thórarin from Seydisfjord came down across the heath, and another man with him. They remained there over night, and had much talk with Helgi. They wanted to be friends with one another. Helgi said to Thorkel, "Where do you expect to go from here?"

He replied, "To Bjorn, at Ness; this winter he sold my linen; I shall be there for three nights."

Then said Helgi, "I wish that we two might travel together over the mountain." Thorkel said he would gladly do this. Afterwards they all rode together to Midby, and from there Thorkel went out to Ness. Helgi knocked on the door at Midby and Rannveig opened it. Helgi said to her, "Do you wish me to make that division of property between Thorgrím and yourself now?"

"Gladly," replied she. So she summoned witnesses and declared her separation from Thorgrím Fur-cap. She took all his clothes and threw them down in the cesspool. After that they left the place, for it was Helgi's intention to fetch her property away later. They journeyed until time for breakfast at Fannardale.

As soon as they had left, Thorgrím sprang up and took a woolen bed-cover and wrapped it about him, since there was no clothing left. He ran over to Hof where dwelt Thórarin Mouldgrub, a man of some importance. Thórarin said, "Why are you afoot so early, Thorgrím, and so scantily clad?"

He answered and reported that his wife had been taken from him; "and now I want to ask you to help me in this affair."

Thórarin replied, "First I will give you some clothes, for that is most necessary now."

Thorgrím ate breakfast there.

Thórarin said, "It is my advice that you seek Helgi Ásbjorn's son and call on him to get redress in your case. And if it goes as I think, and you don't obtain this from him, then ask him when he intends to make good on what he said at the autumn meeting at Thinghofdi. And if he is not aroused by this, then try something else, and tell Helgi Ásbjorn's son that Helgi Droplaug's son will journey up over the mountain in three days' time, seven men all together. Go to Helgi this evening and [don't] get there late, for he himself locks the doors every night at Mjófaness."

They parted, and Thorgrím took his way to Mjófaness the same evening. Helgi was sitting by the fire. Thorgrím laid his errand before him, and told of his trouble, but he received no answer from Helgi. Then Thorgrím said, "The time is drawing very near when you can no longer protect your followers against insults from Helgi Droplaug's son, whether at the Thing or at other gatherings of men. This I must bring home to you. For that matter, when do you expect to have that encounter with Helgi which you promised him at Thinghofdi, when you said that both of you would not get away from the field alive? Or do you wish to be worsted by him again?"

Helgi Ásbjorn's son replied, "Is this your counsel, or that of other men?"

He replied, "Thórarin Mouldgrub advised me."

Then Helgi said, "Very well, Thorgrím, you shall go up over Háls ridge[29] to Mýrar to see Bjorn the White and ask him to come hither before mid-day tomorrow; and then go back over Bolungar field and see the sons of Hallstein at Vídir fields and bid them come here if they wish to avenge their father. Then go down west of the lake to Ossur in the farm at Ás and bid him come here; and you go along with him." Thorgrím set off at once.

During the day the men whom Helgi had sent for came to Mjófaness. Two Norwegians were staying with Helgi; one of them was called Sigurd Skarf, and the other, Onund. Now the sixteen men came to Hofdi; here Helgi asked Hjarrandi and his brother Kári to go with him. He answered, "I was ready long before this."

They were now eighteen all told, and they rode up along Eyvindardale to Knútusel and there lay in wait for Helgi Droplaug's son. Ígul was the name of a man who dwelt under the Skagafell in Eyvindardale; his son was Thórd, and these two were set to spy upon the course taken by Helgi Droplaug's son, since from there one could see men coming more readily than from the spot where Helgi and his followers were.

10. THE FIGHT IN EYVINDARDALE

Now it is to be told that Thorkel came to Fannardale and joined the band of Helgi Droplaug's son, and they remained there over night. Helgi was uneasy in his sleep and he was awakened three times in that night. Thorkell asked him what he had dreamt. Helgi answered, "I shall not tell."

Now they dressed themselves. Helgi asked Thorstein to see that Rannveig was taken care of, "and conduct her, if you will, to the house of my brother Grím."

They rode out of Fannardale before day, up on the heath, and they were nine all together. When they had reached the heights, Helgi rested, for he was exhausted, and he laid his cloak under him. He scratched his cheek and rubbed his chin and said, "Very likely before evening there will be some scratching here. Well now, are you still as eager as you were last night to hear my dream, Thorkel?"

Thorkel replied, "I want to now no less than I did then."

"It seemed to me," said Helgi, "that we were riding on the road by which we are now traveling, and on down along Eyvindardale to Kálf's Hill; there, eighteen wolves, or it may be twenty, charged upon us, and one was larger than the rest. We wished to reach the Hill but could not. They ran at us at once, and one of them bit me in the chin and teeth, and then I was awakened."

Then Thorkel said it was sure that "men are lying in wait for you; it is likely to be Helgi Ásbjorn's son and other men of the district, for your overbearing manner has provoked the hatred of most people in these parts. We two have wanted to be friends, and it is my wish that you come home with me and remain there for a time."

Helgi replied, "I shall go on as I have intended."

They went on down along Eyvindardale and came to the dwelling of Thordís; she was old, and both ugly and black. Helgi meant to ask news of her, but at that moment one of the men made a snowball hard in his hand and threw it at her and hit her on the cheek. She became angry and said, "May the devil take you all!"

"THE DREAM OF HELGI DROPLAUG'S SON."

Helgi said, "It is foolish to hit at a woman. Your worst enemies are on your own side."

So Helgi heard no news there. They left the place and came down to Válagils Creek. Thorkel offered to accompany Helgi to Eyvind River. "There is no need for that," said Helgi.

So they separated, but when Thorkel had come up into the hills a short way he turned back and joined Helgi again. Helgi welcomed Thorkel joyfully and said that was a great proof of friendship.

Then they went on to the sand banks by Kálf's Ford and there they saw eighteen men running towards them. Helgi and his men wished to get up on the hill above, but they could not. Then they left the path and made their way up on to the edge of the gorge by which Eyrargils Creek flows. There was some higher ground there, with a snowdrift below, but now brushwood grows all over that hillock, and there is a little cairn of stones where the fight occurred.

Now Helgi asked his brother Grím whether he wished to hurl his spear at Helgi Ásbjorn's son above or below, and Grím chose to cast it above.

"Then you don't want to have my namesake dead," said Helgi, "for he will have no protection from his shield at the spot where I shall strike him."

Now they both struck at Helgi Ásbjorn's son at once, and Grím pierced his shield, but Helgi was not wounded by his spear. But Helgi Droplaug's son hit his kneecap and the spear glanced down and split his shin-bone downwards through the instep, and so Helgi was disabled at once. Then Bjorn the White sat down and gave support to his shoulders; neither of these two fought that day. Ossur of Ás turned aside also; he said he would not fight against Helgi Droplaug's son, and he sat apart. Thórd Skarf had been spying for Helgi Ásbjorn's son; he had been lying in the water and his clothes were frozen. He struggled up the snowdrift to attack Helgi Droplaug's son, thinking he had good cause to fight him, and as he came onto the drift, Helgi Droplaug's son hurled his spear between Thórd's legs and pierced the scrotum, and he fell down backwards. But the spear stuck in the snowdrift, and he on it, and he hung there on the drift the whole day long.

After that Helgi Ásbjorn's son egged his wife's kinsman to the attack. He called on Hjarrandi, who charged on Helgi together with Kári while Hallstein's sons and one other man attacked Grím. Thorkel Black-Skald was attacked by the two Norwegians and by Sigurd, who was the third best fighter in the band of Helgi Ásbjorn's son. Then here fell Thorkel Black-Skald, but he slew one of the Norwegians and wounded Sigurd badly, for Thorkel was the best fighter of their band, barring Helgi and Grím.

Now the fighting became very bitter, and when Hjarrandi and Kári were charging upon Helgi Droplaug's son, Helgi the Thin of Straum ran against Kári; they struggled together until Kári fell, but Helgi was badly hurt. Hjarrandi pressed hard on Helgi Droplaug's son and hewed at him often and hard, but Helgi struck back no less and no gentler, yet his sword was of little good. Then Helgi said to Hjarrandi, "You'd strike with all your might if your wife were a free-born daughter of Helgi Ásbjorn's son."

Hjarrandi answered, "As far as that goes, both daughters are equally related to Helgi." And he pressed on harder than ever, though these words had intervened.

The shield of Helgi Droplaug's son was badly cut, and he saw it was of no use to him that way. Then Helgi showed his dexterity in warlike feats: he cast aloft his shield and sword and grasped the sword again with the left hand, and he struck at Hjarrandi with it, hitting the leg above the knee; but the sword did not cut when it reached the bone; it glanced down to the hollow of the knee. From that wound Hjarrandi was made unfit for battle. But at the same moment he struck at Helgi. Yet Helgi raised his shield and the sword glanced and struck his face and hit the lower teeth so that the lower lip was cut off. Then said Helgi, "I never was handsome, and you haven't improved my looks now!"

Then with his hands he clapped his beard into his mouth and bit on it. But Hjarrandi slid down the snowdrift and sat down below. It is said that the encounter of Helgi and Hjarrandi would have been shorter if Helgi had had his own

sword, and had not had to deal with several men at once;
yet Hjarrandi too was a dauntless man.

Then Helgi saw that his brother Grím was fallen, but all
those who had attacked him were dead. Grím was lying deadly
wounded. Then Helgi took the sword Grím had used and said,
"Now that man has fallen whom I held most dear; my namesake will hardly wish us to end the fight yet." So Helgi rushed
down the slope to where Helgi Ásbjorn's son was sitting. All
the men had scrambled down from the snowdrift, for none
wished to stand up against Helgi.

"I see you standing there, Ossur," said Helgi, "and against
you I won't defend myself, for it was you who sprinkled me
with water[30] as a child." And with that he came down
from above towards Ossur. Now Ossur had to decide quickly,
for it was a question of death for one or the other of the
two Helgis. His decision was to thrust his spear against
Helgi Droplaug's son so that it went through him. Helgi
pushed himself on to the spear and said, "Now you have betrayed me."

Ossur saw that Helgi was rushing towards him and was
about to reach him with his sword, and he let go of the spear
and the man on it; then the shaft stuck in the ground, and he
let go of it. When Helgi saw that he could not reach him, he
said, "Now I was a bit too slow, but you were too fast!"

So he staggered down on the snow, and that was the end
of Helgi Droplaug's son.

Five of the men in the band of Helgi Ásbjorn's son got
their death, and all the rest were wounded except Bjorn the
White and Ossur. Thorkel Black-Skald fell on the side of
Helgi Droplaug's son, together with his companion and the
Norwegian who had left with Helgi; likewise Helgi's brother
Grím.

11. HOW GRÍM'S LIFE WAS SAVED

HELGI ÁSBJORN'S SON rode away after the encounter, supported on horseback, but Hjarrandi rode alone. Kári was
carried home to Hofdi on shields and a burial mound was
piled over him. When they reached Hofdi, people asked them

for news, and they told them what had happened. One man asked: "What deeds did Helgi Droplaug's son perform today beyond other men?"

Sigurd Skarf answered, "If all the men with Helgi had fought like him, none of us would have escaped alive."

Helgi the Thin came to Eyvind River and told Gróa the news. He was badly wounded himself. She said to her son Bárd, "Take the horses and sledge cart, and let us go and fetch Helgi and Grím."

They rode until they came to the spot where the fight occurred, and here the brothers were laid on the sleigh, and Thorkel with them. But the wounded men rode home on horseback. They buried there the men who were dead. So they took their way home, and Gróa followed closest by the sleigh that Grím was in, and bade them proceed gently with him. When they reached home they had the bodies placed in a storehouse. Gróa said, "Now, my son Bárd and I will lay out the bodies for the night before burial; the rest of you take those that are living and give them care."

When all were lying asleep, Gróa journeyed over the lake to Ekkjufell,[31] where Alfgerdr the Leach dwelt. Gróa asked her to come over to her place with her, and told what had happened. So both returned to Eyvind River, and there was still life in Grím. Alfgerdr cared for his wounds and took him away with her.

The next day a burial mound was made out by the Eyvind River south of the farm; and Bárd carried the bodies thither, together with a man whom they trusted to keep to himself the knowledge that Grím was still alive. Here Helgi and Thorkel were buried.

Grím lay ailing with his wounds that winter, and so did Helgi Ásbjorn's son. Now the report was noised about that Grím was still living; some said it was true, but others that it was not so. It was started by one of Gróa's household. Helgi had a locked bed-closet made for himself in Mjófaness when he heard that Grím had recovered. Later Grím went north to Thorkel Geitir's son at Krossavík, and he was well received there.

12. GRÍM'S SECRET JOURNEY

Now Helgi Ásbjorn's son bought land at Eid[32] out in the district, and sold Mjófaness; he thought he was better lodged where he had his Thing followers living round about him, and here too he had a closed bed made. His wife Thordís asked why he wished rather to have land out there, where the buildings were all surrounded by woods, and none could see men approaching close to the farm yard. Then Helgi spoke a verse,

> 1. Speer I in night's silence oft—
> as skald I speak—fore-
> tokenings[33] that tell of
> evil soon betiding me;
> foes (they warn) in forest—
> fighters battle-skilled—are
> hither bound, spear-bearing
> 'gainst one, battle-ready.

Grím remained at Krossavík several winters. He was downcast, and he never laughed again after Helgi's death.

Thorkel once had an errand in Eyjafjord, to reconcile some followers of his at the Thing, and so he left home; but Grím remained there and busied himself about the homestead. Some nights later Grím made ready to leave, and said he was going to see about a debt from a man named Thorgrím who lived at Hjardarhagi in Jokulsdale.

"It is clear," said Grím, "that he doesn't mean to pay."

Then spoke Jórun, the wife of Thorkel, who was the daughter of Einar at Thver stream, "I will pay the debt for you; do not go."

"Then he won't be the one to pay it," said Grím. So he departed, taking some provisions with him.

His foster-brothers Glúm and Thorkel Crane went with him. They rode until they came to Rang River west of the Fljót. Here they swam the water with Thorkel Crane, and they came to a homestead called Bakki, west of the Fljót. They went into the cowshed and took a shovel and spade, and then they journeyed on to Oddmarsbrook, west of Eidaskóg. There by the brook-side they dug themselves an underground cave, and shoveled all the dirt out into the brook. They wished to have a refuge there if they were in need of it.

13. GRÍM'S REVENGE

ON THE very day when they were by the brook, people left the Thing at Lambaness,[34] and many men went to Eid with Helgi Ásbjorn's son. Ketilorm was a man who dwelt at Hrollaug- stead; he rode with Helgi and had thirty men with him. Bjorn and Hjarrandi, the kinsman of Helgi by marriage, were also there.

That same evening Grím and his fellows came out of their cave and went to Eid farm. They entered the door of the cowshed, whence a passage led into the dwelling. Here they stood and looked in to observe what was going on in the house.

In the evening Helgi Ásbjorn's son said to his wife, "Where do you intend to have Ketilorm and his wife sleep?"

She replied, "I have made ready a good bed for them in the room outside the hall."

Helgi answered, "They shall lie in our bed, for they yield theirs to us every time we are there."

Thordís replied, "You aren't always as cautious as you might be! If I were in Grím's place I should try to attack you just when there were most guests here, and you are busy looking after things."

He said, "I am often reproached for being too cautious." So he had his way about the beds, and not she.

Then Grím said to Thorkel, "Now you go in and see if you can get the sword that Thorbjorn whetted, which was once the sword of my brother Helgi."

Thorkel went in, and when he came back he had the sword with him. A little later Grím said, "Go in now and see where Helgi and Thordís have their bed."

Thorkel was away for a little time, and then he returned and told Grím that they were sleeping in the room outside the hall in a closet bed with no door to it. A blind man named Arnodd had his bed there, a servant of Helgi and a very powerful man, who lay by the wall opposite to Helgi. Grím said to Thorkel, "I want you to go in and fall upon Helgi, for you are the second man most bound to avenge my brother Helgi."

"That is true," said Thorkel.

Then Grím put the sword into his hand, and together they went to the door. Thorkel took his place there and said to Grím, "I don't want you to think that I am afraid to attack Helgi, yet this seems strange to me, after what you have said—which was that you will permit no man to avenge your brother's death except yourself."

"The reason for it is this: there will always be some hope of avenging my brother so long as I am alive myself."

Then Thorkel started to go in, but Grím took hold of him and said, "You are a brave lad, Thorkel; yet I am not sure that you would give Helgi as deep a wound as I might wish. Let it be as you said: it is true that I begrudge any other man the right to avenge my brother's death."

Then Grím took the sword and said, "Do you, Thorkel, hold fast the door-ring, for I trust you most of all to remain unafraid; but Glúm shall shoot the bolt." Before Grím went in, he took a short winding stick in his hands. He was clad in a shirt and linen trousers, but he wore no shoes on his feet.

He entered the hall, and he knew that there was a pile of firewood by the door leading into the cowshed. But earlier that evening Glúm had tied together the tails of all the cattle in the shed.[35] Grím went and stood in the space beside the bed of Helgi and Thordís. Here he laid down what he had in his hands, and then he approached the bed and drew the covers from Helgi. He awakened at this and said, "Did you touch me, Thordís? Why is your hand so cold?"

"I didn't touch you," she replied; "but you are very unwary. I fear that something serious is about to happen."

After that they fell asleep again. Then Grím went up to Helgi and moved away the arm of Thordís, which she had laid over him.

Grím said, "Awake, Helgi! You have slept enough!" And with that he fell upon him with the sword so that it went quite through him.

Helgi cried, "Wake up, you men in the hall! Someone is murdering me!"

Then Grím took the piece of wood where he had laid it, and cast it on the pile of firewood so that it tumbled down. All the men in the hall leaped to their feet, and they thought the killer had run in the direction where they heard the noise. But Grím turned to the door by which he had entered. There a man grasped him about the middle and lifted him up on his chest. It was Arnodd. He cried, "This way; I've got the rascal!"

Grím said, "Curse you for holding me back! Let me go! I was about to avenge Helgi!"[36]

Then Arnodd felt him with his free hand, and noticed that he was barefoot and clad [as if for bed] in linen trousers. He released Grím. Afterwards he said, "I let him go because I didn't know that it would have been better to hold him."

Then Grím ran to the door and got out; Thorkel closed it and Glúm shot the bolt. After that they went to their cave and hid there.

Those who remained behind took counsel and decided to keep watch at all the fords and lie in wait at the bridges over the Jokul River. Hjarrandi and Ketilorm and Helgi's kinsmen went out first on the search. Most of them returned from it while Helgi Ásbjorn's son was still living, and he asked if Bjorn and Hjarrandi had come back.

"Here I am," said Bjorn.

"It is still true, then," said Helgi, "that Hjarrandi shows the greatest manhood for my sake." Then he died.

Now the night passed, and Grím and his men came up out of their cave and went up along the shore to Hofdi, and there they saw a tent. Grím approached the tent and said, "Why do you let thieves come by your ship?"

Thorlák was the name of the man who owned the ship; he was accompanying some Norwegians. He lent Grím his boat, and so the men were rowed over. Grím took back the boat, and then swam over the lake. Thence they went along the shore until they reached the Jokul River, and here Grím and Thorkel swam over, while Glúm went on alone.

They journeyed north to Krossavík, and here Thorkel had not yet come home. People asked them for news, but they said they had none to tell.

Next day Grím was playing chess with a Norwegian, and a
boy of Thorkel's and Jórun's knocked against the table and
upset the boards. The Norwegian kicked at the lad, and the
boy broke wind. Grím burst out laughing.

Jórun came up to him and said, "What has happened to
you on your trip that you are able to laugh now? What news
do you have to tell?"

Then Grím spoke a verse:

> 2. The lindens-of-gold[37] laughed
>   loudly at Grím—though
>   small was the joy—as
>   in the south he lay stricken;
>   but otherwise echoes
>   their outcry—they've heard now
>   of free-giver's[38] fall—from
>   fells of the Fljót-land.

"Doesn't that mean," asked Jórun, "that you have avenged
your brother Helgi?"

Then Grím spoke another verse:

> 3. Revenge, methinks, I've rightly
>   enow wreaked on the spear-
>   shaft's wielder[38]—hewer
>   of Helgi to his bane;
>   now let Bjorn the bold one—
>   blade bit raven-feeder[38]—
>   think to counter-wreak the
>   kinsman I have killed.

"It will now turn out," said Jórun, "that we are indeed
unprotected when the husbandman is away. And yet we might
both take the risk, if it weren't that Bjorn, Helgi Ásbjorn's
son's kinsman, lived so close to us."

Grím and his fellows remained concealed there until Thorkel came home. When he arrived he asked Grím what had
happened, and for the details of the killing of Helgi. Grím
told him how it came about, and he spoke a verse:

> 4. Stinger-of-the skull[39] there
>   straight through struck him—that

was done by Helgi—hewed he
a hero to the bone;
then the warrior, stricken
by the strife-blood's-serpent[40]
bored was through the breast with
a blow—it was his bane.

5. Hero-wise fought Helgi there
and hardily—men heard it
bruited wide—the brands did
on the brynies sing;
gladdener-of-ravens[41] gave—
gloated he in combat—
thrusts, and three he wounded
of the thronging foe.

6. Steerer I of sea-steeds[42]
eight days stayed alone;
for the task betimes done
in terror I did tarry;
I, the sword-play-ruler,[43]
swift, with staff-of-wounds[40]
thirled the gold-dispenser,[37] and
my thrust at him went through.

Thorkel now rode to the Thing, but Grím stayed in a tent
on the mountain called Snæfell[44] up above Krossavík, and
his companions with him.

14. GRÍM'S FLIGHT TO NORWAY

HRAFNKEL the *godi*, a cousin of Helgi Ásbjorn's son, took
up the case of manslaughter against Grím. Thorkel Geitir's
son offered to pay indemnity for Grím, but Hrafnkel would
not take it, so Grím was declared outlaw, and people returned
home from the Thing.

That summer a ship came to Krossavík, owned by Norwegians. The steersman accepted hospitality for the winter
from Thorkel, taking three men with him. When autumn
came, Grím came down from the mountain to a ledge of rock,
and there was a large pile of stones above his tent, and also

one below it, and that was at the upper limits of the grassy slopes. It has been called Grím's place ever since. The Norwegians came to play games at Krossavík, and visit the steersman. One of them said, "I think I see a tent up on the mountain, or else a gray rock; but it seems to me it is a tent."

Thorkel answered, "You have very sharp eyes. That is a rock, and we call it the tent-stone." So they said no more about it.

The next night Thorkel came up to Grím and said, "People are likely to be coming up the mountain soon, and I wish that you would go back to Arneidarstead. Ingjald your kinsman is a resourceful man, and he will take good care of you. But if he thinks it too difficult, come back here again."

So Grím and his companions went to Ingjald, and hid in the cave which is now called after Grím. Ingjald said to his shepherd, "Pay no heed, even if some of the sheep disappear."

Later a housemaid said to Ingjald, "Our brooklet is so dirty that we can hardly drink out of it."

"The reason for that is that it was dammed," said he, "but I have been cleaning it out."

But the truth of it was that Grím had dug out an underground passage, and the outlet was by his wife's bed, and there he lay at night; but the earth from it was thrown into the brook.

Thorkel the Wise lived in Njardvík. He spied out many hidden things. He was a near kinsman of Grím's. Hrafnkel the Godi gave him a hundred[45] pieces of silver to spy out where Grím had found refuge. He did not have many friends. This Thorkel journeyed up into the district over the mountains, up along the eastern shore of the Lagarfljót, and down again on the west. So he came to Arneidarstead. Grím had a son six years old. Thorkel met the boy and said to him, "Are you Grím's son?"

"Yes, I am," said the boy.

"Is your father at home?" asked Thorkel.

"I do not know, and I wouldn't tell even if I did."

That evening one of the women asked: "Where is Grím's bucket? I cannot find it."

Thorkel said, "What's this about Grím's bucket?"

Just then Ingjald joined them and said, "They call our goat Grím, and he is watered with that bucket."

With that Thorkel thought he could be sure that Grím was there, and he departed and told Hrafnkel how matters stood.

Ingjald and Thorkel Crane left home in the latter part of spring and rode south around the glaciers until they came down to Hornafjord.[46] A ship was berthed there. Here Ingjald took passage for Grím and all his people and also for Thorkel Crane, and gave the skipper money to keep the matter quiet; and Grím and his people were to come there in secret. After that Ingjald went home, and a little later he conducted Grím's party to the ship so that no one was aware of it, and Ingjald remained by the ship until they put out to sea. Then Ingjald returned home.

Hrafnkel became certain that Ingjald had helped to save Grím, and Ingjald paid three silver[47] marks for this. Grím and his fellows steered to Sogn in Norway. Then Thorkel the skipper said to Grím, "I won't begrudge you food, but I don't trust myself to protect you against Gunnar the Norseman[48] nor any of those who wish you dead."

Then Thorkel bought horses for Grím and his men, and gave them a guide into the Uppland district. He and Grím parted good friends. They journeyed until they came to a man named Finngeir; he was a young man and rich. His sister was called Sigrid; she was fair and very skillful. Grím and his men remained there over night. Finngeir asked Grím, "Where do you intend to go?" Grím told him how things stood. "Stay here for a fortnight, then, if you wish," said Finngeir.

When the time had passed, Finngeir said, "I want you to take over the farm that my brother had, Grím, and your people with you; if you want to remain here, treat it as if it were your own."

Grím accepted this offer.

15. THE DEATH OF GRÍM

GAUS was the name of a turbulent viking. He had three companions, and they did much dishonor to many people;

scarcely any steel could wound them. Gaus had been in the Upplands for several winters; he had driven two husbandmen away from their farms and settled there himself. After that he asked for Sigrid, Finngeir's sister, in marriage, but she would not have him. Then Gaus challenged Finngeir to a holmgang.[49] Finngeir answered, "I'd have nothing against that, if I were only four years older; even so I'll fight with you rather than give my sister to you."

Finngeir made an offer of money to any man who would fight against Gaus, and promised to give his sister to the one who would kill him, but no one would do it. Then Grím accompanied Finngeir to the island, and offered to fight for him. Gaus came with his men, and he staked six marks in silver as pledge.[50]

"I will take that money," said Grím.

Grím had two swords with him, for Gaus knew how to blunt the edges of blades.[51] Grím fought equally well with both hands. He flourished a sword with his left hand, but he struck at Gaus with the right and cut off his leg above the knee. So Gaus fell, but as he did so, he struck with his sword at Grím and the blow hit his leg, so that he received a flesh wound. Then the viking ran away, but Grím took over the silver, and he was highly praised for this deed. Finngeir gave Grím the house he was holding, with all the possessions that went with it, both land and livestock.

Grím's wound became infected, and the leg swelled up. One evening a woman came thither who said she was a leach; she offered to bandage Grím's wound, and they let her do it, and after that she went away. A little later, Grím's leg swelled up until it was affected all the way up to the belly. They sent for the priest, and Grím received the last rites; and afterwards he died. But the woman's name was Gefjon the Witch. She had been the leman of Gaus.

The winter passed, and in the spring Finngeir bought a ship for Helga and she journeyed back to Iceland with all her possessions, and Thorkel Crane went with her. They came to Reydarfjord. Ingjald went out to meet his daughter, and took her home to Arneidarstead, and she lived there from that time on. Helga gave Thorkel half ownership of the vessel, and half she sold to the Norwegians. The following spring Thorkel left Iceland, and there is no more to be said of him.

Thordís, who had been the wife of Helgi Ásbjorn's son, was married to Hauskuld the son of Thorgeir the Godi at Ljósa Lake. Hauskuld seized Glúm, who had been with Grím Droplaug's son when Helgi Ásbjorn's son was slain, and they had him killed. After Ingjald's death Helga remained at Arneidarstead with Thorvald, her son by Grím.

Thorvald had a son named Ingjald. His son was called Thorvald, and it is he who told of these happenings. It was in the year following the arrival of Thangbrand the Priest[52] in Iceland that Helgi Droplaug's son was killed.

Notes

NOTES ON THE SAGA OF GUNNLAUG
AND HRAFN

1. The Stockholm MS has introductory lines claiming *Ari prestr inn fródi* as the teller of the saga.

2. G. Vigfusson and F. York Powell, *Corpus Poeticum Boreale*, Oxford, Vol. II, p. 442. Hrafn is also named as poet to Óláf the Swede.

3. A. G. Brodeur, *The Prose Edda*, The American-Scandinavian Foundation, 1929, p. 177. The verse is number 19 in this translation. The original verse does not name Helga or Gunnlaug.

4. *Hallfredar Saga* contains a reference to that conversation (Chap. 10 of my translation) in which Hallfred tells Gunnlaug about Hrafn's courtship of Helga. *Hallfredar Saga* records the fact that Hrafn has obtained Helga. E. Ó. Sveinsson, *Íslenzk Fornrit*, Reykjavik, 1939, Vol. VIII, p. 196. This volume contains *Vatnsdoela Saga, Hallfredar Saga, Kormáks Saga*.

If *Hallfredar Saga* is earlier than the saga of Gunnlaug, then this fact would lend some support to the existence of Helga, provided that *Hallfredar Saga* were completely authentic.

Nordal and Jonsson date this version of the story of Gunnlaug between 1270 and 1280, although it does not exist in manuscript until much later. S. Nordal and G. Jónsson, *Íslenzk Fornrit*, Reykjavik, 1938, Vol. III, p. LX. Vol. III contains the *Borgfirdinga Sǫgur*.

Sveinsson, *op.cit.*, p. LXXIII, thinks that the version of *Hallfredar Saga* may be dated about 1220.

Finnur Jónsson, however, dated the *Saga of Gunnlaug* as early as 1200.

5. Vigfusson and Powell, *Origines Islandicae*, Oxford, 1905, Vol. I, p. 60.

6. Verse 10 in my translation reveals an antagonism between Gunnlaug and Hrafn which does not necessarily arise from rivalry in love. In fact, it gives the impression that Hrafn has been belittling Gunnlaug.

7. The verse is number 20 in this translation. It is attributed to the poet Kormák, who applies it to Steingerd. The verse is number 3 in *Kormáks Saga*. Sveinsson, *op.cit.*, p. 209.

In his notes to the saga, Small claims verses 23 and 24 as spurious. L. S. Small, *Gunnlaugssaga*, Leeds, 1935.

8. In their edition of the saga, Nordal and Jónsson discuss at length the verses and also the question of a relationship be-

tween the story of Gunnlaug and other Icelandic sagas, particularly the *Saga of Hen-Thórir*, the *Saga of Hallfred, Laxdalers' Saga*, and the *Saga of Bjǫrn the Dales-champion.*

See also M. Schlauch, *Romance in Iceland*, London, 1934. In a letter this year, Professor Schlauch drew my attention to resemblances between the story of Gunnlaug and the Irish tale of Deirdre.

I feel that there is a danger of making too much of the indebtedness of one saga to another. Perhaps we should recognize the existence of a common stock of situations, descriptions, and verses on which the narrators could draw freely.

9. According to Nordal and Jónsson, *op.cit.*, p. 53, this farm was not under Valfell at all.

10. Fylgjur—animal materializations of the spirits of men. To see one of these animals in danger was a sign that the man with whom it was associated would shortly be in danger. In *Njáls saga* we are told that Thord once saw a goat, covered with blood, lying in a hollow. Njál could not see the animal, but he explained to Thord that this must be his *fylgja* and that he had better watch out for himself. G. W. Dasent, *The Story of Burnt Njál*, Dent, 1931, Chap. 41.

For a useful survey of Norse conceptions of death and the soul, the reader should consult H. R. Ellis, *The Road to Hel,* Cambridge, 1943.

Another excellent book on Norse customs and beliefs is *The Viking Age* by P. B. Du Chaillu, Chas. Scribner's Sons, 1890.

11. Nordal and Jónsson, *op.cit.*, p. 55, remark on the similarity between this interpretation of the dream and an interpretation given by Gest, son of Oddleif, in *Laxdalers' Saga.*

12. Exposure of children seems to have been fairly common. The usual procedure was to place a child to be exposed in a shallow grave. Deformity was a frequent cause of exposure. Du Chaillu, *op.cit.*, Vol. II, p. 39, assembles some useful evidence from the sagas about exposure.

13. For a full description of buildings and their interiors consult Du Chaillu, *op.cit.*, Vol. II, p. 241.

14. In those days youngsters seem to have matured rapidly. Harald Fairhair succeeded to his father's kingdom at the age of ten, and we read in *Heimskringla* that he was then "bigger, stronger, and more handsome than other men." E. Monsen and A. H. Smith, *Heimskringla*, D. Appleton and Company, 1932, p. 42. This translation of *Heimskringla* is probably the best in English, and it has very full notes. For the convenience of the

reader who does not easily understand Old Icelandic, I have given references to this work rather than to an edition of *Heimskringla* in Old Icelandic. (See also note 29.)

15. A.D. 1000.

16. *Audun Festargram. Garmr* was the Northern Cerberus. The sons of Ósvíf were banished from Iceland for their attack on Kjartan, son of Óláf. When Audun refused to take the men on board, Ósvíf prophesied his death from drowning.

17. Thorstein has perhaps been talking about Önund, but the MSS have lost the reference. It may be, however, that Gunnlaug has introduced the name of a well-known man himself in order to strengthen his argument.

18. Thorstein killed two of Steinar's servants for trespassing on his property. This, with other matters, was brought up at the Assembly, and Thorstein's father, who was chosen to settle the business, ordered Steinar to leave the district. S. Nordal, *Íslenzk Fornrit*, Reykjavik, 1933, Vol. II, *Egils Saga*, p. 277ff.

19. See Nordal and Jónsson, *op.cit.*, p. 67, for a note on the resemblance between this reply and that of Snorri in *Eyrbyggja Saga*.

20. Helga is not betrothed to Gunnlaug, although later he behaves as if she had been. Thorstein promises only that Helga shall not be betrothed to anyone during the next three years. She is to be betrothed to Gunnlaug after three years, if Thorstein is still willing.

In a regular marriage procedure the settlement of the bride's dowry and of the suitor's own property was arranged first. Then the agreement was announced to witnesses, and the betrothal followed. The betrothal was binding. The normal length of a betrothal was twelve months. See Du Chaillu, *op.cit.*, Vol. II, p. 10, for full information on the ceremony of marriage. *Frostathing's Law*, established by Hákon and Earl Sigurd, sets the length of the period of the betrothal.

21. Hákon was killed in a pig-sty.

22. A.D. 978-1016. The English have not shared Gunnlaug's view of Ethelred the Redeless.

23. Gunnlaug was named after his grandfather. See Chap. 4, paragraph 1, of this translation.

24. Gunnlaug declares that he must visit "the house-wall of the steeds of three kings and two earls, as I promised the owners of the land." This is not in keeping with his visits as they are related in the saga.

25. Sigtrygg was King of Dublin. His third wife was Korm-

lad. He was killed in 1014 at the Battle of Clontarf. For a concise account of events leading to this battle consult E. Curtis, *A History of Ireland*, Methuen, 1936, Chap. 2.

26. This is a poem in Runhenda, i.e., with end-rhyme.

27. Earl Sigurd was also killed at Clontarf.

28. According to *Heimskringla* this was the wealthiest part of Sweden.

29. Sigríd. Vissivald of Russia and Harald of Grǫnland wooed Sigríd. She thought herself too good for them, and she had them burnt—"Sigríd said that this would warn petty kings from other lands against coming to woo her." Monsen and Smith, *op.cit.*, p. 150, and *Ór Óláfs sǫgu ins helga inni sérstǫku*, B. Adalbjarnarson, *Heimskringla* ii, in *Islenzk Fornrit*, Reykjavik, 1945, Vol. xxvii.

30. Before Christianity reached Sweden, spring (*at gói*) sacrifices were held at Upsala for peace and victory. After the coming of Christianity, the Assembly was held at Upsala. B. Adalbjarnarson, *op.cit.*, p. 109. Monsen and Smith, *op.cit.*, p. 280.

31. Gunnlaug is referring to the type of verse known as a *flokkr*. This was a poem which had no refrain. Gunnlaug himself had recited a poem in *drápa* form, i.e., a heroic poem with a refrain. Gunnlaug is suggesting that Hrafn is insulting the king. The episode illustrates very clearly the nature of Gunnlaug's "serpent's tongue."

It is strange that such important verses are not recorded.

The reader interested in Old Norse poetry should refer to Lee M. Hollander's book, *The Skalds*, Princeton University Press for The American-Scandinavian Foundation, 1945. On the meter see E. Sievers, *Altnordische Metrik*, in *Paul's Grundris*, 1905, Vol. ii.

32. See Du Chaillu, *op.cit.*, Vol. i, p. 535, on legal procedure. *Njáls Saga* gives much information about the law.

"It is a law that there shall always be a man in our country whose duty it is to tell people the law . . . to be elected on that Friday before the cases are proclaimed. . . . It is also a law that it is the Law-speaker's duty to recite all parts of the law in three summers." *Grágás I*, quoted by Du Chaillu, *loc.cit.*

33. According to *Heimskringla*, Hallfred was given his nickname by Óláf Tryggvason. Monsen and Smith, *op.cit.*, p. 178. (For a different account of the episode of the sword-poem see E. O. Sveinsson, *op.cit.*, p. 161.)

34. Emendation from *Hreduvatn*, by Nordal and Jónsson, *op.cit.*, p. 87.

35. Thórodda was the wife and not the mother of Torfi. Nordal and Jónsson, *op.cit.*, p. 88, suggest that in the manuscript at this point there is a scribal error for *Thorkell*.

36. It does not appear that Helga divorced Hrafn, although she could have done so quite easily according to the Icelandic laws at that time.

37. This was in the year 1007. Nordal and Jónsson, *op.cit.*, p. LIX, give a useful chronological table of events in the saga.

Egils Saga and *Kormáks Saga* contain much information on the rules of dueling.

There were two main types of duel: *einvígi*, which had no set rules; *hólmgang*, which had an elaborate code of rules.

There was also a queer kind of duel known as a "tub-fight." Two men would get into a tub and fight there with sticks or swords. Vigfusson and Powell, *Origines Islandicae*, Oxford, 1905, Vol. II, p. 636.

38. In *Njáls Saga* there is a similar incident. Mord has refused to fight with Hrút and gets hooted for it. Later on, in Hrút's presence, two children play the game of being Mord and Hrút at the Assembly. See Dasent, *op.cit.*, p. 166.

39. Every family had the right to claim an indemnity for the slaying of one of its members. The payment of the indemnity bought off revenge.

Du Chaillu, *op.cit.*, Vol. I, p. 544, assembles much information from the sagas on the matter of compensation or indemnity.

40. This is the only known reference to this man.

There is no evidence outside this saga for any children of Helga and Thorkell, although an attempt was made in the seventeenth century to make a list of their possible descendants. For a reference to this attempt see Nordal and Jónsson, *op.cit.*, p. 106, note 3.

41. Lines 5-6 are not recorded.

"I laid the pole of gold rings dead in my arms . . . God took the life of the linen-goddess . . . to him desirous of gold . . . it is more bitter to live on."

To the Icelander of the early eleventh century, poetic diction was often a useful cloak for emotion. We, in the twentieth century, have no vocabulary which can be called exclusively poetic. Perhaps there was an approach to such a vocabulary in England in the eighteenth century.

NOTES ON THE SAGA OF THE
EIGHT CONFEDERATES

1. Midfjord opens up in the southwestern coast of Húnaflói, on the north coast of Iceland. Much of the action of the saga is centered about Mel, modern Melstaðr, located inland from the southern extremity of Midfjord. Reykir farmstead, still so called, lies close by. See Kålund, *op.cit.* (in note 1 to *Droplaugarsona saga*, below), II, pp. 5f. and 10.

2. Skard farm settlement was located inland from the southeastern part of Skjálfandi, a bay to the northeast of Midfjord on the northern coast.

3. Ásgeir's Creek is in Víðidale, which lies southwest of Hóp bay at the southern extremity of Húnaflói.

4. *Vadmal* (Icelandic *vaðmál*), woolen homespun material, was used in reckoning values such as prices and wages. The unit was an ell (*alin*), about half a yard in length.

5. That is, Horn Strands on the northwest extremity of Iceland.

6. MS K here gives a better reading: "he never went farther north than to Eyjafjord, nor farther west than to the Hvít River [i.e., into Borgarfjord on the west coast], but oftenest to Hrútafjord."

7. Modern Borðeyri, towards the head of Hrútafjord on the western shore; still a center of trade.

8. See note 1. This had been the home of Kormák the Skald half a century before.

9. Skridnesenni farm between Bitrufjord and Kollafjord, so called from the mountain of that name which rises to the northwest of the entrance to Hrútafjord.

10. Grettir Ásmund's son is the hero of the well-known *Saga of Grettir the Strong (Grettis saga)*, composed in the fourteenth century. Many of the events in it are based on folklore, with considerable use of the supernatural, but there is also authentic information about historical persons. See Chap. 14 for a reference to our saga by name.

11. The office of *godi* (Icelandic *goði*) included functions of judge in local matters, leader of the community, representative of its interests at the assembly or Thing, and pagan priest in the era before Christianity. For a short account of it see James Bryce, "Primitive Iceland," in *Studies in History and Jurispru-*

dence, Oxford University Press, 1901, pp. 263ff., especially pp. 268-71.

12. Svalastead in Vídidale. See note 3.

13. As the passage implies, it was unusual for a woman to do this; the father or nearest male kinsman generally arranged a betrothal.

14. That is, the meeting had been declared sacred or inviolable. This was the formal opening of the session.

15. Thórarin of Langádale was nearest kin of Óspak's wife Svala; hence he was involved in Óspak's affairs. See Chap. 4.

16. The second adjective is an addition by emendation, based on the reading in MS K and justified by the pointed use of the three terms (not two) later in Ófeig's speech.

17. That is, one ounce of silver to each.

18. The brother of Gunnlaug Ormstunga, hero of the saga in this volume that is named for him.

19. Self-judgment was the privilege awarded to a successful party in a lawsuit, by which he could fix the damages on the losing side.

20. Laugardale, still so called, lies east of the Thing plains (Thingvellir). Reydarmúli, now called Reydarbarm, is a mountain to the east of the plain; Bláskógi Heath was the name then applied to the region around it to the north, west and south. See Kålund, *op.cit.*, I, p. 156f.

21. Note that this verse is not composed in the formal and elaborate skaldic *dróttkvætt* represented in other stanzas. (For a description of this measure see Hollander, *The Skalds*, p. 9f.) The simpler stanza here represented may be regarded as a more popular form. It was called *fornyrðislag*.

22. Borg settlement on Borgarfjord, which opens up from Faxaflói on the west coast.

23. Literally, "gods of riches," a kenning for "warrior" or "chieftain."

24. A kenning for "warrior."

25. Idi's "laughter" or "mouthful" is a kenning for gold because of this story: Idi, the giant son of Ölvaldi, along with his brothers Thjazi and Gang, inherited a treasure from his father. The three decided to measure their patrimony by taking a mouthful each at a time. "And we have a metaphor among us now," says Snorri Sturluson in his *Prose Edda*, "to call gold the mouth-tale of these giants." Translation by A. G. Brodeur, New York, 1923, p. 92.

26. The implication is, of course, that Odd would do some pillaging at Borg, once he reached Borgarfjord.

27. The balanced sentence structure points to imitation of foreign (Latin) style.

28. Harald Sigurd's son, called Hardrádi, reigned 1046-1066; see the Introduction.

29. For the stanzaic form, see note 21. The last two lines are proverbial. They refer to the belief that wild beasts devour one another until only the tail is left.

30. The phrase in the original (*i mínu máli*) is unclear; ms K lacks it.

31. There is an implied insult: that the household was reduced to eating the flesh of horses that had died naturally. The eating of horse meat was later forbidden.

32. The Rang River (Rangá), district lies southeast of the one where the Thing plains are located. For the site of the local Thing, see Kålund, *op.cit.*, I, p. 218.

33. Literally, "bushes of metal," a kenning equivalent to "trees of armor," i.e., "warriors."

34. Dwarves and giants, represented in the original verse by the proper names Am and Austri, are said to have made a reconciliation with the giant Suttung by offering him a draught of mead made from the blood of Kvasir mixed with honey. Because Kvasir had been a wise man especially created by the gods, this drink imparted the gift of poetry. Hence "dwarves' and giants' drink" or "drink of Am and Austri" is a kenning for poetry. For the story, see the *Prose Edda*, Brodeur translation, p. 93.

35. Thorgeirsfjord is a small inlet on the north coast of Iceland, eastward of Eyjafjord, actually so slight an indentation of the coast that sea breezes would be easily perceptible in it. The name may be a scribal error.

36. One would expect a favoring wind to come from the west, since the purpose was to sail eastwards. The phrase does not occur in ms K.

37. Valfell and the other places here mentioned are in the region of the Hvít River which empties into Borgarfjord on the west coast.

38. For the stanzaic form, see note 21.

39. Borgarhól is not known today. It must have been located in Vídidale, near Svalastead; see Kålund, *op.cit.*, II, p. 24.

NOTES ON THE SAGA OF
DROPLAUG'S SONS

1. The valley of Skrida (Skridudale) opens up from the body of water, the Fljót or Lagarfljót, near which most of the action occurs. This is a long and narrow lake, at places little wider than a river, which is fed from the south by the Jokul and Kelda Rivers, and flows northward, emptying into Héradsflói (on the northern part of the east coast of Iceland). Fljótsdale is a valley at the southern end, near the juncture of the tributaries with the lake. Húsastead no longer exists. See Kristian Kålund, *Bidrag til en historisk-topografisk Beskrivelse af Island*, 1879-1892, II, p. 243n.

2. Konungahella is at the mouth of the Göta River in southwest Sweden. The geography of this incident is confused, reflecting fictional origin.

3. "Hundred," here as elsewhere, means a "great hundred" or 120 in our system.

4. The Vík may be Oslo Fjord, if a proper name is here intended.

5. In the west, in Borgarfjord, near the mouth of the Hvít River.

6. The district north of the Hvít River and west of its tributary the River Brú. Burfell still exists in the southwestern part of the district, near the mountain of the same name.

7. Still located not far from Hallormstead, to the east of the Lagarfljót.

8. For the term *godi*, see note 3 to the *Saga of the Eight Confederates*.

9. Atlavík, not far from Hallormstead, is still so called.

10. The settlement was north of the river, not far from the point where it empties into the northern (lower) part of the Lagarfljót.

11. Bessastead (Bessastaðir) is in Fljótsdale, not far from Brekka.

12. Vídi (Willow) fields (Víðivellir) and other places mentioned here are in the valley of the Jokul River.

13. Not to be confused with the Droplaug for whom the saga is named.

14. This Hrafnkel was the grandson of the famous Hrafnkel Freysgodi, the chief figure in a saga named for him. See the translation by Gwyn Jones in *Four Icelandic Sagas*, Princeton

University Press for The American-Scandinavian Foundation, 1935. The last chapter shows the relationship with Helgi Ásbjorn's son here briefly indicated.

15. Mýrar is in the southern (upstream) part of the Fljót area, south of Hallormstead.

16. A settlement still found northward (downstream) from the juncture of the Jokul River with the Fljót.

17. Mýness is in the northern (downstream) area of the Eyvind River, not far from Finnstead, eastward of the Fljót.

18. This reference to the causes of a magic storm is of especial interest for the student of early Icelandic folklore. Walking about a temple or sacred object with or contrary to the sun's motion ("sunwise" or "widdershins") is elsewhere reported to have such effects. See the story contained in the Old Irish "Wooing of Emer" as translated by Lady Augusta Gregory in *Cuchulain of Muirthemne*, London, 4th ed., 1911, p. 28. Here a Queen walks counter-sunwise around a magic well to show contempt for it, whereupon the waters rise out of it and pursue her. The report of this magic storm in the saga made something of an impression in Iceland. It is cited from the saga in a document of the Bessastead church (A.D. 1203); see *Diplomatarium Islandicum*, I, 1857-1876, p. 340f.

19. Tunga is the tongue-shaped area lying between the Fljót and the Jokul á Brú River to the west of it.

20. This is tantamount to an accusation of bribery.

21. This district is eastward of the mouth of the Fljót, inland from Borgarfjord. Desjamoor (Desjamýri) is still an important settlement.

22. That is, in the territory lying between Herrádsflói (into which the Fljót empties) and Lónsvik to the southwest of it on the east coast.

23. A small fjord south of Mjófifjord on the east coast. Thingmúli, at which meetings for the district were held, lies inland westward of the head of Reydarfjord.

24. A reminder of Hrafnkel's success in the suit to force Helgi to share the *godord* (*godi's* office) with him. See Chap. 4.

25. That is, Helgi expects to pile a cairn over his namesake's corpse.

26. See note 3.

27. In Vesterdale, inland from Vapnfjord and Nýpsfjord.

28. There is an inconsistency here. In Chap. 6 it is said that Thorstein lived at Desjamoor.

29. Between Skridudale and Fljótsdale.

30. In pre-Christian times the act of sprinkling a child with water completed the formal recognition that it was accepted as a member of the family. The father, by refusing to lift up a newborn child that was presented to him, could legally reject it. He was usually the person to do the sprinkling; here, however, an outsider (Ossur) apparently did.

31. Ekkjufell, still so called, lies east of the Fljót opposite Egilstadir.

32. Eid, still so called, is situated east of the Fljót near its northern extremity.

33. The meaning of the word in the original (*argspæing*) is in doubt. Conjectures are necessary at several points in this verse; the whole is freely translated.

34. The precise location is unknown. Apparently it was east of the Fljót.

35. It is surmised by Jakobsen, in his edition of the text (p. lxi) that the original version gave more information about Glúm. His role in the entire episode is undeveloped. His death is briefly recorded at the end of the saga.

36. He means, of course, his brother Helgi; but Arnodd would suppose he was referring to the other Helgi, just wounded by him.

37. Literally, "destroyer (i.e., dispenser) of gold," kenning for "chieftain."

38. A kenning for "warrior."

39. Literally, "hard wolf of the skull," a kenning for "sword."

40. Another kenning for "sword."

41. A common epithet for "warrior."

42. "Sea-steeds" are ships; the whole is a kenning for "warrior."

43. Another kenning for "warrior."

44. The name Snæfell is no longer applied to any hill or mountain in this region. See Kålund, *op.cit.*, II, p. 199. It must have referred to one of the Krossavík mountains.

45. See note 3.

46. Hornafjord is on the eastern coast, southwest of the territory in which the action of the saga occurs.

47. Each mark was the equivalent of eight silver ounces.

48. Probably the Gunnar Thidrandi's Bane of whom a separate saga is told.

49. A holmgang was a combat, traditionally held on an island, used as a means of settling disputes. For a full account of the rules and procedure, see the *Saga of the Sworn Brothers*, trans-

lated by Lee M. Hollander, Princeton University Press for The American-Scandinavian Foundation.

50. This pledge would serve to ransom his life if he lost.

51. The ability to blunt an enemy's weapon is a magic power often attributed to berserks.

52. Thangbrand the Priest was the first Christian missionary in Iceland. He arrived in A.D. 997. See the introduction to this saga.